Study Guide

for use with

Business Law
with UCC Applications

Twelfth Edition

Gordon W. Brown
North Shore Community College

Paul A. Sukys
North Central State College

McGraw-Hill
Irwin

Boston   Burr Ridge, IL   Dubuque, IA   New York   San Francisco   St. Louis
Bangkok   Bogotá   Caracas   Kuala Lumpur   Lisbon   London   Madrid   Mexico City
Milan   Montreal   New Delhi   Santiago   Seoul   Singapore   Sydney   Taipei   Toronto

The McGraw-Hill Companies

Study Guide for use with
BUSINESS LAW WITH UCC APPLICATIONS
Gordon W. Brown and Paul A. Sukys

Published by McGraw-Hill/Irwin, an imprint of The McGraw-Hill Companies, Inc., 1221 Avenue of the Americas, New York, NY 10020. Copyright © 2009, 2006, 2001, 1997, 1993 by The McGraw-Hill Companies, Inc. All rights reserved.

1 2 3 4 5 6 7 8 9 0 BKM/BKM 0 9 8

ISBN: 978-0-07-334115-6
MHID: 0-07-334115-0

www.mhhe.com

Contents

To the Student

This study guide is a student support supplement to the Twelfth Edition of *Business Law With UCC Applications*. It provides a variety of involvement and application exercises to assist you in achieving the objectives of this course of study. Each chapter in this workbook can be completed successfully in formal class sessions; with an instructor who serves as a facilitator, consultant, or general resource person; or in independent study.

Before you begin to use this guide, you should familiarize yourself with its basic features. You will note that each chapter begins with a fill-in "Outline," followed by a "Legal Concepts" activity, a "Language of the Law" vocabulary review, and an "Applying the Law" series of case problems. Each of these activities has independent instructional value. However, used together, they can make it easier for you to succeed in achieving the goals of this course. Consistent and systematic review and study of the text in conjunction with the activities in this guide may also help to improve your scores on tests and examinations.

Completing this study guide is an answer key to the "Legal Concepts," "Language of the Law," and "Applying the Law activities. It is recommended that you attempt to answer all exercises before referring to the answer key for confirmation of your responses.

The fill-in "Outline," which begins each chapter, offers a summary of the major points covered in that chapter. This outline correlates to the outline presented in each chapter opener in the text and may be used as a study aid or as an indicator of subject mastery. Answers are not provided for this activity. If you cannot fill in a blank, use your text to locate the appropriate response. Although this activity is suggested for each chapter of the text covered, its completion is *not* a substitute for a thorough reading and review of that chapter.

The "Legal Concepts" are true-false statements designed to gauge your understanding of the concepts and principles introduced in the text. Completion of this activity will enable you to diagnose your strengths and weaknesses in mastering important concepts of law and help point out subject areas and topics presented in the text that require your further study.

"Language of the Law" is an activity that will help you to develop a working knowledge and understanding of key legal terms presented in the text. Strengthening your vocabulary will help you become more conversant and confident in classroom discussions concerning business law topics. This activity will also assist you in becoming familiar with, and retaining comprehension of, terms you may encounter in your future business and legal relationships.

"Applying the Law" enables you to make immediate use, through interpretation and analysis, of principles learned in the text. You will find these cases ideally suited for classroom discussion because they are open to differing interpretations and opinions. This will help you to recognize and appreciate the fact that the law is not ironclad but subject to varying interpretations and applications.

This study guide has been produced both to test your comprehension of terms and concepts covered in the *Business Law With UCC Applications* text and to provide you with a quick and easy means of reviewing important chapter material. We wish you the best of luck in your course of study.

Gordon W. Brown
Paul A. Sukys

Chapter 1   Ethics

Chapter Outline

1-1 Defining the Law, Morality, and Ethics

    A. The law consists of _____
_____
_____

    B. Morals are _____
_____
_____

    C. Natural law theory sees law as _____
_____
_____

    D. Positive law theory says _____
_____
_____

1-2 Ethical Theories

    A. Ethical Relativism says _____
_____
_____

    B. Social Contract Ethics holds _____
_____
_____

    C. Utilitarianism says _____
_____
_____

    D. Rational Ethics rejects _____
_____
_____

    E. Role Model Ethics encourages _____
_____
_____

1-3 Social Responsibility in the Business Sector

    A. The greatest force in the American industrial state is _____
_____
_____

    B. Corporations have great power because _____
_____
_____

C. Corporations should exercise social responsibility because:

1. _____
   _____

2. _____
   _____

3. _____
   _____

1-4 The Relationship Between Law and Ethics

A. The law is needed because _____
   _____

B. Ethical considerations should _____
   _____
   _____

Ethical Concepts

For each statement, write **T** *in the answer column if the statement is true or* **F** *if the statement is false.*　　　**Answer**

1. Most legal textbooks begin by defining the law.　　1. _____
2. Morals are values that govern a society's attitude toward right and wrong.　　2. _____
3. The law can stop a person from doing wrong.　　3. _____
4. Natural law sees law as originating from outside, superior forces.　　4. _____
5. The theory of ethical relativism claims that there are unchanging standards of right and wrong.　　5. _____
6. Ethical relativism is not a common position among Americans.　　6. _____
7. The character trait of honesty means that a person is always open and truthful.　　7. _____
8. Compassion means that people should always act with the intent of doing good.　　8. _____
9. A prescriptive theory describes the values at work in a social system.　　9. _____
10. Utilitarianism always focuses on consequences.　　10. _____
11. In utilitarianism, actions are always stated in terms that are emotional.　　11. _____
12. Utility thinking is the same as cost benefit thinking.　　12. _____
13. Codes of ethical conduct are often complex and difficult to follow.　　13. _____
14. Rational ethics rejects the notion that ethical rules can change.　　14. _____
15. Laws are established by the government.　　15. _____

Language of the Law

Select the ethical term that best matches each definition.

a. Compassion
b. descriptive theory
c. ethical relativism
d. fairness
e. honesty

f. Law
g. integrity
h. morals
i. prescriptive theory
j. rational ethics

k. Role model theory
l. social contract ethics
m. utilitarianism
n. utility thinking

Answer

1. An ethical theory that claims that there is no constant and unchanging standards of right and wrong.

1. _____

2. The values that govern a society's attitude toward right and wrong.

2. _____

3. A set of rules established by the government to maintain harmony, stability, and justice.

3. _____

4. An ethical character trait that promotes justice and equal treatment.

4. _____

5. An ethical character trait that promotes truthfulness.

5. _____

6. An ethical character trait that is related to courage.

6. _____

7. An ethical character trait that allows people to be sympathetic to one another.

7. _____

8. A theory that explains how to come up with the values of a society.

8. _____

9. A theory that encourages people to pattern their behavior after admirable individuals.

9. _____

10. A theory that holds that right and wrong are measured by an implied agreement in a society.

10. _____

Applying Ethical Theories

1. Muller was sent to a foreign country by his company Rifkin Textiles, Inc., to arrange for the sale of several million dollars of material to a foreign retail firm. Before finalizing the deal, Muller was told that the retailers expected to receive large bribes to sign their names to the contract. Muller agreed to pay the bribes, despite the fact that he would never do so if the deal were negotiated in the United States. Name and explain the ethical system that Muller appeared to use to make his decision.

_____

_____

_____

_____

2. Tuttle was asked to explain how he would go about determining his ethical stance in regard to the death penalty. Tuttle offered the following statement, "Kill anyone who kills another person." What ethical character traits might Tuttle have ignored? Explain.

_____

_____

_____

_____

3. Karu told his twelve-year-old daughter not to bring home art supplies from school without asking the teacher because that type of conduct is unethical. Karu then explained that if she just told him what she needed, he would take the supplies from the storeroom at work. What ethical character traits might Karu have ignored? Explain.

_____

_____

_____

_____

4. LaRue found an old shopping bag containing $550. LaRue, who was out of work and desperately in need of cash, turned the bag over to the police. When she was asked why she had turned the money in, LaRue said that she did it because that's what she would want someone to do if it were her money. Name and explain the ethical guideline that LaRue used in making the decision.

_____

_____

_____

_____

5. While watching a public television show on ancient civilizations, Alonso learned that certain cultures exiled their people to the wilderness when they became too old and feeble to be productive. Alonso declared that such a practice was right. When asked why she believed that it was right, she replied that she had no sympathy for such people. What ethical character traits might Alonso have ignored? Explain.

_____

_____

_____

_____

6. Gunderson applied for a job as the financial vice president of a small Midwestern college. In the last position that she held at a small Southwestern college, Gunderson made several faulty investments that caused that college to lose $10 million. Because no one asked her directly about this issue during the interview for the new job, Gunderson failed to mention the problems that she caused in her previous position. Which of the ethical character traits did Gunderson violate? Explain.

_____

_____

_____

_____

7. Lowell, the president of a small industrial company, found that she must lay off several workers because of a slow down in the market. Instead of basing her decisions on who to lay off on either seniority or merit, she decided to lay off only those people that she did not particularly like. Which of the ethical character traits did Lowell violate? Explain your answer.

_____

_____

_____

_____

8. Moore, a shareholder in Northshore, Inc., (NI) discovered that the board of directors of NI had voted to turn down a proposed merger plan with West Central Industries. Moore sued the directors claiming that their vote had caused her shares to drop in value. The directors argued that they were looking out for the local economy because West Central had planned to shut down NI's facilities in the town of Centerville. What arguments can the board use to defend this position? Explain.

_____

_____

_____

_____

9. Fred Harrington has had a great deal of trouble with George Ferris, one of his workers, who failed to show up for work for several days in a row. When Ferris does return to work, rather than firing him Harrington talks to him and finds out that Ferris has a health problem that has interfered with his work schedule. Harrington then offers to adjust Ferris' work schedule. What ethical character trait has Harrington used here? Explain.

_____

_____

_____

_____

10. When Hackett learned that the company for which she worked was going to go bankrupt, she saw a chance to take several pieces of expensive equipment without anyone knowing about it. Nevertheless, Hackett decided not to remove the equipment. When asked why she did not, Hackett said that she avoided the temptation because that's what she would want someone to do if the equipment belonged to her. Name and explain the ethical guideline that Hackett used to make the decision.

_____

_____

_____

_____

Chapter 2   Sources of the Law

Chapter Outline

2-1 The Purpose and Operation of Law

A. The law consists of _____

_____

_____

B. The three primary objectives of the law are:

    1. _____

_____

    2. _____

_____

    3. _____

_____

C. The law's status as a complex adaptive system explains _____

_____

_____

2-2 Constitutional Law

A. A constitution is _____

_____

B. The first three articles of the U.S. Constitution establish the structure and operation of the federal government.

    1. Article I establishes _____

_____

    2. Article II establishes_____

_____

    3. Article III establishes _____

_____

C. The amendments to the Constitution establish _____

_____

_____

2-3 Statutory Law

A. A statute is_____

_____

B. Statutes are arranged and catalogued for easy reference.

    1. A code is _____

_____

_____

_____

2. A title is _____

_____

_____

_____

C. The Uniform Commercial Code is _____

_____

_____

D. E-Commerce is _____

_____

_____

2-4 Court Decisions

A. Common law is _____

_____

_____

B. Statutory interpretation is _____

_____

_____

C. Judicial review is _____

_____

_____

2-5 Administrative Regulations

A. Administrative law is _____

_____

_____

B. Congress passed the Administrative Procedure Act to _____

_____

_____

C. The Federal Register is _____

_____

_____

Legal Concepts

For each statement, write **T** *in the answer column if the statement is true or* **F** *if the statement is false.*

Answer

1. The law has but one purpose, to maintain order.

   1. _____

2. The present U.S. Constitution is the only constitution that the United States has ever had.

   2. _____

3. The U.S. Constitution is the supreme law of the land.

   3. _____

4. All states are required to adopt uniform laws.

   4. _____

5. The common law tradition started in England.

   5. _____

6. Courts may not interpret legislation by filling in the gaps in statutes. 6. _____

7. The first ten amendments to the U.S. Constitution are known as the
Declaration of Independence. 7. _____

8. A title is a subdivision of a code. 8. _____

9. Article III of the U.S. Constitution authorizes the creation of the
federal court system. 9. _____

10. A court cannot interpret a statute unless it is presented with a case that
involves that statute. 10. _____

11. The Uniform Commercial Code (UCC) was written by Congress. 11. _____

12. Persuasive precedent must be followed by a court. 12. _____

13. The power of judicial review belongs to Congress. 13. _____

14. Congress can create administrative regulations but the state
legislatures cannot. 14. _____

15. The Administrative Procedures Act was repealed in 1996. 15. _____

Language of the Law

Select the legal term that best matches each definition.

a. administrative law
b. binding precedent
c. code
d. common law
e. complex adaptive system
f. constitution
g. constitutional law
h. constitutional supremacy
i. cyberlaw
j. devolution
k. law
l. preemption
m. statute
n. title
o. Uniform Commercial
Code

Answer

1. A single law or a series of laws that deals with some aspect of
computers. 1. _____

2. A network of interacting conditions. 2. _____

3. A model case that a court must follow when presented with a
similar case. 3. _____

4. The basic law of a nation or state. 4. _____

5. A compilation of all the statutes of a particular state. 5. _____

6. The process by which the courts shift the duty to enforce a right
from an upper level authority to a lower one. 6. _____

7. A law passed by a legislature. 7. _____

8. The process by which the courts decide that a federal statute must
take precedence over a state statute. 8. _____

9. A subdivision of a code. 9. _____

10. The body of law generated by administrative agencies. 10. _____

Applying the Law

1. Dennison, a citizen of Littleton, New Hampshire, believed that her rights had been violated under the guidelines established by a state statute. She later read that a New Hampshire Supreme Court ruling had declared that statute unconstitutional. However, since the ruling had involved a case in Ashland, New Hampshire, she did not believe her case would be affected. She was wrong. Why?

_____

_____

_____

_____

2. Wesleyan, the president of radio station WHYR, was about to file several routine forms with the Federal Communications Commission (FCC). She then found out that a new regulation issued by the FCC might require her to file several additional forms. After the regulation went into effect, Wesleyan refused to comply. She argued that the FCC had too much power and that Congress had done nothing to curb that power. She was wrong. Why?

_____

_____

_____

_____

3. The National Conference of Commissioners on Uniform State Laws (NCCUSL) developed a revised version of Articles 3 and 4 of the Uniform Commercial Code. LaForge believed that once the NCCUSL had written the revisions, they automatically became law in his state. He was incorrect. Why?

_____

_____

_____

_____

4. Kennilson, a judge in a New Jersey state court, had a case before her that required her to interpret a state statute. Her law clerk pointed out that the New Jersey Supreme Court had recently interpreted that same statute. Kennilson said that she did not have to read that case because courts do not have to rely on precedent when engaged in statutory interpretation. Kennilson was wrong. Why?

_____

_____

_____

_____

5. Raskob was a public defender working for the City of Cleveland. In that role, he wrote and sent an e-mail to the *Cleveland Plain Dealer* in which he criticized his boss, Tom Knapp, the City Law Director, and in which he questioned the truthfulness of several witnesses at a recent trial. When Raskob was fired, he sued the city, arguing that his First Amendment rights had been violated. Knapp argued that the power to control the right of free speech in relation to public employees on the job had devolved to the state and according to state law he could fire Raskob. Why was Knapp correct?

_____

_____

_____

_____

6. Lawson was arrested under a local ordinance that made it a crime to hold a political meeting if the participants were not affiliated with either the Republican or Democratic parties. Lawson claimed that the U.S. Constitution forbid such a prohibition. He argued that it violated the First Amendment's guarantee of freedom of assembly. The sheriff argued that the local ordinance did not have to comply with constitutional principles. The sheriff was incorrect. Why?

_____

_____

_____

_____

7. The Pierce Corporation, headquartered in Delaware, agreed to purchase several shipments of steel from the Viking Steel and Tube Company, located in West Virginia. When Viking decided not to deliver the steel after all, Pierce sued. Lawyers for Viking said that the law regarding commercial transactions in West Virginia was totally different from the law regarding commercial transactions in Delaware. The lawyers for Viking were incorrect. Why?

_____

_____

_____

_____

8. Loeb was arrested under a Wyoming statute that made drug addiction a crime. At trial, Loeb claimed that such a statute was invalid. When the Supreme Court of California declared a similar California statute invalid, Loeb argued that this decision was a binding precedent that the trial judge in his case would have to follow. Loeb was incorrect. Why?

_____

_____

_____

_____

9. A state statute held that it was illegal to make any negative comments about public officials. *The Loudonville Star* printed a negative news story about the Loudonville police chief. The chief then had McFly, the editor of *The Star,* arrested under the authority of the statute. McFly argued that the statute conflicted with the Constitution. The chief argued that the conflict with the U.S. Constitution did not matter, as long as the statute was in line with the state constitution. The chief was incorrect. Why?

_____

_____

_____

_____

10. Werner, who worked for a large insurance company, used the company's computer to uncover some confidential matters about his neighbors. A state statute made it an unlawful invasion of privacy for unauthorized individuals to read the contents of these confidential records. The statute, however, did not specifically mention using a computer to explore confidential records. Werner argued that the court had no power to interpret the statute to include using a computer to invade private records. Werner was wrong. Why?

_____

_____

_____

_____

Chapter 3   The Judicial Process

Chapter Outline

**3-1   The Court
System**

A. The federal court system is authorized by_____
_____
_____

    1. U.S. district courts are courts of_____
_____
_____

    2. The thirteen U.S. courts of appeals include
        a. _____
        b. _____
        c. _____
    3. The U.S. Supreme Court is the court of final jurisdiction in all
    cases appealed from _____

B. The courts of each state are organized according to _____
_____
_____

C. Electronic jurisdiction is _____
_____
_____

**3-2   Civil
Procedure**

A. A civil lawsuit begins when a plaintiff files a complaint against a
defendant.
    1. A plaintiff is _____
_____

    2. A defendant is_____
_____

    3. A complaint is_____
_____

B. In the next stage of a civil lawsuit, a copy of the _____
_____ and a(n) _____ must
be given to the defendant.
C. In the next stage of a civil lawsuit, the defendant has a certain
amount of time in which to file a(n) _____
_____

D. During the pretrial stage of a lawsuit, several activities can be carried out, including

1. _____

_____

2. _____

_____

3. _____

_____

E. During the process of *voir dire,* the attorneys _____

_____

F. In an opening statement, an attorney presents_____

_____

G. A verdict is_____

3-3   Criminal Procedure

A. A criminal case begins when the defendant is arrested and has a(n)

_____

B. A preliminary hearing is a court proceeding during which_____

_____

_____

C. Formal charges may be brought in two ways, by indictment or by information.

1. An indictment is _____

_____

2. An information is _____

_____

D. An arraignment is a court proceeding during which _____

_____

_____

E. In a criminal trial, the prosecution must prove that the defendant is guilty beyond _____

Legal Concepts

For each statement, write **T** *in the answer column if the statement is true or* **F** *if the statement is false.*

Answer

1. A court's jurisdiction is usually limited with respect to territory and type of case.

   1. _____

2. Each state and territory in the United States has at least two U.S. District Courts.

   2. _____

3. U.S. District Courts have jurisdiction over cases involving federal law only.

   3. _____

4. The U.S. Supreme Court has appellate jurisdiction only.

   4. _____

5. As a general rule, a federal court hearing a diversity case will apply principles of general law.

    5. _____

6. Most states have state courts that are lower than the general jurisdiction courts.

    6. _____

7. A complaint will always ask for money from the defendant.

    7. _____

8. In the answer the defendant will never admit anything.

    8. _____

9. Pretrial conferences are only held to discuss the possibility of settlement.

    9. _____

10. The objective of discovery is to simplify the issues at trial and to prevent unnecessary arguments and surprises at trial.

    10. _____

11. Prospective jurors may be rejected if they have a financial interest in the outcome of the trial.

    11. _____

12. The instructions are given to the jury by the judge.

    12. _____

13. A criminal defendant enters a plea at the initial appearance.

    13. _____

14. An information is a set of formal charges brought by a grand jury.

    14. _____

15. The defendant has the burden of proof in a criminal trial.

    15. _____

Language of the Law

Select the legal term that best matches each definition.

a. affirmative defense
b. answer
c. arraignment
d. complaint
e. deposition

f. discovery
g. ESI
h. information
i. interrogatories
j. plaintiff

k. preliminary hearing
l. prosecutor
m. removal
n. summary judgment
o. writ of execution

Answer

1. Oral statements made out of court under oath by witnesses or parties to a lawsuit

    1. _____

2. Sending a case from state to federal court

    2. _____

3. The person who brings a lawsuit by filing a complaint

    3. _____

4. The defendant's official response to the complaint

    4. _____

5. A formal court proceeding during which the defendant pleads guilty or not guilty

    5. _____

6. The process by which the parties to a civil lawsuit search for information relevant to the case

    6. _____

7. The attorney who represents the government in a criminal case

    7. _____

8. A court procedure during which the judge decides whether probable cause exists to continue to hold a criminal defendant

    8. _____

9. Written questions that must be answered under oath by the opposite party in a civil lawsuit

    9. _____

10. The term used by the federal court to refer to computer evidence

    10. _____

Applying the Law

1. Morgan brought suit in state court against Lynch alleging certain violations of state contract law. Along with these allegations, Morgan also accused Lynch of certain federal antitrust law violations. Lynch wanted the case sent to federal court. Morgan argued that such a move was not permitted under the rules of the court. Morgan was wrong. Why?

_____

_____

_____

_____

2. Franzetta, a citizen of Vermont, was the subject of several outright lies in a book written and published by Franklin, a citizen of Georgia. Franzetta decided to sue Franklin in U.S. District Court in Georgia. Franzetta asked the court for $45,000 in damages for losses suffered as a result of Franklin's lies. Franklin argued that this case does not belong in federal court. She was right. Why?

_____

_____

_____

_____

3. Fred Bunker, a citizen of Montana, sued Allan Stivic, a citizen of Colorado, in the U.S. District Court in Colorado in a diversity action. The amount in controversy was $120,000. Bunker argued that principles of general law, rather than Colorado state law, should apply in the case. He was incorrect. Why?

_____

_____

_____

_____

4. Queen was injured when a bridge collapsed in Bellville County. He sued Bellville County for not maintaining the bridge properly. During discovery, Queen asked his attorney to have several key witnesses respond to a series of interrogatories. She refused. Why?

_____

_____

_____

_____

5. Bogan was a prospective juror in a case involving a boating accident. While examining the potential jurors prior to trial, the plaintiff's attorney found out that Bogan owned a boat. Since the outcome of the case might result in higher insurance rates for boat owners, the attorney asked the court to dismiss Bogan. The court refused to do so. Why?

_____

_____

_____

_____

6. Cascio witnessed a barroom brawl that led to a lawsuit. When the plaintiff lost the case at trial, he appealed it to the intermediate court. Cascio was afraid that she would have to testify again in front of the appeals court. Her fears were unfounded. Why?

_____

_____

_____

_____

7. Janeway sued Kirk after Kirk injured Janeway in an automobile accident. When Kirk lost the case, he told Janeway that he owned no property and could not pay the judgment from either his wages or his checking account. How can Janeway compel Kirk to pay the judgment?

_____

_____

_____

_____

8. Seigret was arrested on charges of disorderly conduct. She was brought before a judge for a preliminary hearing. While she was waiting for the judge, she was told by Bernard that she would have to enter a plea of guilty or not guilty at this hearing. Bernard was incorrect. Why?

_____

_____

_____

_____

9. Tupperman's criminal case was brought before the grand jury. Tupperman believed that he would be able to testify on television during the grand jury proceeding. He was incorrect. Why?

_____

_____

_____

_____

10. Krauss's criminal case went to trial. He believed that his attorney had the burden of proving that he was innocent of all charges. Krauss was wrong. Why?

_____

_____

_____

_____

Chapter 4   Alternative Dispute Resolution

Chapter Outline

4-6 A Primer on Alternative Dispute Resolution (ADR)

A. Alternative dispute resolution occurs whenever _____
_____
_____

B. The ADR option deals with the following problems:
  1. _____
  2. _____
  3. _____

C. The ADR option can provide_____
_____

D. Critics of ADR point out _____
_____
_____

4-7 ADR Techniques

A. Mediation is _____
_____

B. Arbitration is _____
_____

C. Med-Arb is_____
_____

D. Early neutral evaluation is _____
_____

E. Summary jury trials are _____
_____

F. Private civil trials are _____
_____

4-8 Proactive ADR

A. Partnering is_____
_____

B. ADR contract clauses are_____
_____

C. Settlement week is _____
_____

D. Negotiated rule making is _____
_____

E. Post-Appellate procedures involve _____
_____

F. International arbitration agreements involve _____

_____

G. The science court is _____

_____

Legal Concepts

For each statement, write **T** *in the answer column if the statement is true or* **F** *if the statement is false.*

6. The adversarial system is not the only alternative available for legal problem solving.

6. _____

7. Litigation can be expensive because of the initial steps that lead to the filing of a lawsuit.

7. _____

8. Alternative dispute resolution (ADR) can provide an economical and efficient alternative to litigation.

8. _____

9. Alternative dispute resolution techniques are without problems.

9. _____

10. Mediation and arbitration are the same thing.

10. _____

11. Arbitration hearings are run like trials, but without the safeguards and assurances that come with the rules of civil procedure.

11. _____

12. Med-Arb combines the best aspects of mediation and arbitration.

12. _____

13. A verdict rendered in a summary jury trial is binding.

13. _____

14. Private civil trials have their own rules of procedure.

14. _____

15. Construction contracts are ideally suited to partnering agreements.

15. _____

16. There is only one form that can be used for an ADR contract clause.

16. _____

17. In a contract negotiation situation, ADR contract clauses benefit the parties in the strongest position.

17. _____

18. Attorneys are not required to be present during settlement week.

18. _____

19. Negotiated rule making involves governmental agencies.

19. _____

20. A national science court was established under the Federal Science Court Act.

20. _____

Language of the Law

Select the legal term that best matches each definition.

f. ADR contract clause	**f.** mediation	**f.** private civil trial
g. arbitration	**g.** mediator	**g.** reg-neg
h. arbitrator	**h.** negotiated rule making	**h.** science court
i. early neutral evaluation	**i.** negotiation	**i.** settlement week
j. international arbitration agreement	**j.** post-appellate procedures	**j.** summary jury trial

Answer

6. An ADR technique in which a third party or parties actually settle a dispute between other parties
    6. _____

7. A pledge to use arbitration should the parties find themselves in disagreement as to the enforcement of the original international contract
    7. _____

8. A shortened version of a trial conducted in less than a day before an actual jury
    8. _____

9. A third party who helps the parties reach a settlement but who does not actually settle the dispute
    9. _____

10. A contract clause that specifies that the parties to the contract have agreed to use an alternative dispute resolution technique when a disagreement arises
    10. _____

11. A trial that is not conducted by the official court but which does follow the same rules of procedure and evidence as trials held under the official auspices of the court.
    11. _____

12. A proposed court that would act as a forum for disputes involving scientific and technological controversies
    12. _____

13. A period of time during which a court clears its dockets of all official business except for attempts to settle disputes
    13. _____

14. A third party who actually settles a dispute between other parties
    14. _____

15. Taking a case that has been rejected by a domestic court to an international organization
    15. _____

Applying the Law

6. Beth Jansen, CEO of the Hoyle and McDevitt Engineering Corporation, entered negotiations with Yuri Carpo, president and chair of the board for Outer Ring Techtronics, Inc., the purpose of which was to develop a particle accelerator for Outer Ring. After engineers at Hoyle and McDevitt built the accelerator, engineering technicians at Outer Ring changed the accelerator's computerized control system. Shortly thereafter, the entire system crashed. Since Hoyle and McDevitt's bill was not paid, Jansen wants to sue Outer Ring but is hesitant to do so because the primary factual issues in the case focus on the engineering modifications. Consequently, she is apprehensive about her belief that a judge and a jury will be lost by the technical jargon that may be used at trial. What alternatives are available to Jansen?

_____

_____

_____

_____

7. Opal Krenshaw, a free-lance artist, entered a work-for-hire agreement with Timeshare, Inc. During the negotiation stages of the agreement, Krenshaw asked that an ADR clause be inserted in the contract that would compel the parties to submit any claim to the American Arbitration Association, which would assist them in selecting an objective moderator who would help the parties decide on an appropriate ADR plan. Would this plan favor Krenshaw or Timeshare? Explain.

_____

_____

_____

_____

8. Zita and Adam Thompson sued the Hill Valley General Hospital and Dr. Pearl Kapital in state court. They claimed that Dr. Kapital had performed an operation on Mrs. Thompson without her consent. Under state law, the case was submitted for mandatory arbitration before trial. The Thompsons lost the arbitration hearing. The case then went to trial. At the trial the hospital asked the court to allow the results of the arbitration hearing into evidence. The Thompsons attempted to block the submission of the arbitration results, arguing that the mandatory arbitration of such claims is unconstitutional. Are the Thompsons correct? Explain.

_____

_____

_____

_____

9. Serious concerns about the dangers associated with the development of a cold fusion reactor arose after an incident that involved a near-accident at the National Fusion Reactor Center. The Nuclear Regulatory Commission held a conference to discuss the level of safety that should be followed in laboratories involved in such research. Those involved in the conference included the researchers themselves, certain fusion energy experts, representatives from organizations involved in similar research, and governmental representatives from the Nuclear Regulatory Commission, the Environmental Protection Agency, and the National Science Foundation. Would this type of situation be appropriate for a reg-neg approach? Explain.

_____

_____

_____

_____

10. Refer back to the details outlined in the fact pattern presented in question 4. Reconsider those facts and answer the following question. Might a science court handle this type of situation even better than an agency's reg-neg procedure? Explain.

_____

_____

_____

_____

11. Janus Industries, Inc. and Gregori Laboratories, Ltd. entered a contract that included an ADR clause. The clause stated that any dispute that arose as a result of the contract would be submitted to arbitration. The clause said that the arbitrator of such a dispute would render a decision that included both findings of fact and findings of law. When a dispute arose, Ingrid Argyle was hired as an arbitrator. Argyle did not make findings of fact or law when her decision was rendered. Would the lack of findings of fact and findings of law as required by the ADR be grounds for the court to revoke the arbitrator's ruling? Explain.

_____

_____

_____

_____

12. David Olsen, owner of the Olsen Building Maintenance Corporation, entered a contract agreeing to repaper all of the walls in city hall for the city of Mount Henry, Montana. When the job was completed, the wallpaper began to come unglued and fall from the walls. The city argued that Olsen was responsible for the problem, while Olsen insisted that the heating system in city hall emitted fumes that cause wallpaper paste to disintegrate. What alternatives are available to Olsen and the city? Explain.

_____

_____

_____

_____

13. The Nebraska Department of Transportation (NDT) was charged with the task of drafting a series of rules to implement the repaving of all secondary roads in the state. Rather than simply writing the rules and placing them before the affected parties, what approach might NDT take? Explain.

_____

_____

_____

_____

14. The Hawaiian State Power Cooperative and the Associated Power Corporation of Hawaii planned to construct a power plant on the island of Oahu. Property owners objected to the way in which their land was appropriated for the project by the government and the power cooperatives. The property owners also objected to the planned location of the power plant because it would interfere with their ability to utilize the land properly. Might a science court handle this type of situation? Explain.

_____

_____

_____

_____

15. When Georgette Danza was discharged from her job with Maxwell Industries, Inc., she was convinced that the firing had been in violation of an implied contract created by Maxwell's employee policy manual. When she brought suit against Maxwell, both sides agreed to hold a summary jury trial. After the trial was held, both sides participated in a post-trial settlement conference. The results of the jury poll indicated that, although the jury had decided the case in Danza's favor, they were unable to agree on the amount of damages. What action will Danza and Maxwell probably agree to next? Explain.

_____

_____

_____

_____

Chapter 5   Criminal Law

Chapter Outline

5-1 Definition and Classes of Crime

    A. A crime is _____
_____
_____

    B. Federal criminal law is authorized by _____
_____

    C. Classes of crimes

        1. A felony is _____
_____
_____

        2. A misdemeanor is _____
_____
_____

5-2 Elements of a Crime

    A. The first element of a crime is _____
_____
_____

    B. The four commonly recognized mental states in criminal law are __
_____
_____

    C. Motive is not _____
_____
_____

    D. Criminal law outlines not only offenses but also _____
_____
_____

5-3 Specific Crimes

    A. Crimes against the people include _____
_____

    B. Crimes against property include _____
_____

    C. Crimes involving business include _____
_____

5-4 Electronic Crimes

A. Electronic trespass is _____
_____
_____

B. Electronic crimes involving computer use include _____
_____

C. Electronic crimes that target computers include _____
_____

5-5 Defenses to Criminal Liability

A. The three tests for determining the insanity of a defendant are
1. _____
2. _____
3. _____

B. Entrapment occurs when _____
_____
_____

C. Justifiable force can include _____
_____
_____

D. In criminal law the concept of mistake is _____
_____
_____

Legal Concepts

*For each statement, write **T** in the answer column if the statement is true or* **F** *if the statement is false.*

                                                                      Answer

1. Crimes are punishable by the official governing body of a nation or state.   1. _____
2. A misdemeanor is punishable by a jail term of six months or less.   2. _____
3. A felony is a crime that can be punished only by imprisonment.   3. _____
4. Some states have separate categories for their most serious crimes.   4. _____
5. Building code violations are generally considered felonies.   5. _____
6. Most states include involuntary actions within the definition of criminal act.   6. _____
7. Refusal to act can sometimes be considered criminal.   7. _____
8. Motive is an essential element of criminal liability.   8. _____
9. Recklessness requires a perverse disregard of a known risk.   9. _____
10. The oldest test of insanity is the M'Naghten Rule.   10. _____
11. People found NGRI automatically go free.   11. _____
12. Defense of others is never a valid defense.   12. _____

13. Some courts consider the battered spouse syndrome defense to be a
    form of self-defense.   13. _____
14. The unlawful touching of another person is called battery.   14. _____
15. Individuals who wrongfully take property entrusted to their care have
    committed larceny.   15. _____

Language of the Law

Select the legal term that best matches each definition.

a. bribery   e. forgery   i. negligence
b. electronic trespass   f. homicide   j. purpose
c. entrapment   g. irresistible impulse test   k. robbery
d. felony   h. larceny

                                                                   Answer

1. The false making or changing of a writing with the intent to defraud   1. _____
2. Carrying away the property of another without the right to do so   2. _____
3. To act with the intent to cause the result that does, in fact, occur   3. _____
4. The act of taking personal property from the possession of another
   against that person's will   4. _____
5. Gaining access to a computer with the intent to commit a crime   5. _____
6. The insanity test that claims that as a result of a mental disease, the
   defendant did not know right from wrong or was compelled to commit
   the crime   6. _____
7. To act with a failure to see the possible negative consequences of the
   action   7. _____
8. The killing of one human being by another   8. _____
9. A corrupt agreement induced by an offer or reward   9. _____
10. A crime punishable by death or imprisonment for a term exceeding one
    year   10. _____

Applying the Law

1. Conrad, a known fence, had approached several people in the neighborhood offering to buy stolen property. Mr. Girard reported this to the police. The police then sent an undercover officer to investigate. When Conrad attempted to purchase stolen goods allegedly in the possession of the undercover officer, the officer arrested him. Conrad claimed he was the victim of entrapment. Was he correct? Explain.

_____

_____

_____

_____

2. While walking in his own neighborhood, Andy Ranier was approached by several young men who demanded money from him. When he refused, they attacked him. Ranier pulled out a gun and shot one of his attackers. Ranier was later charged with attempted murder. Ranier claimed he acted in self-defense. Was he correct? Explain.

_____

_____

_____

_____

3. Georgette McArthur brought her car into the Parker Muffler Shop for a new exhaust system. The shop manager told McArthur that she could pick up the keys to her loaner car at the front desk. By mistake, McArthur took the keys for Claremount's Accord. When Claremount could not find his car, he called the police and reported it stolen. Did McArthur commit the criminal act of car theft? Explain.

_____

_____

_____

_____

4. Jenkins's daughter was raped by Martinique. Martinique confessed to the charges and was given a suspended sentence. Jenkins was in the courtroom when this was announced. In a state of extreme rage, Jenkins killed Martinique. While Jenkins's actions were clearly intentional, they were performed in a state of extreme anger as a result of a reasonable provocation. What crime did Jenkins commit? Explain.

_____

_____

_____

_____

5. Craig Newton was angry at Fred Zimmerman because Zimmerman was promoted to the position that Newton believed was rightfully his. Newton waited for Zimmerman in a dark alley in back of the factory where they both worked. After waiting a while for Zimmerman, Newton attacked and beat a man who turned out to be Ralph Daniels. Newton argued that he attacked Daniels by mistake and should not be held criminally liable. Was he correct? Explain.

_____

_____

_____

_____

6. Henry Thomas was the chief financial officer of Biogenetic International, Inc. Because he was heavily in debt, he wrongfully appropriated funds from the company's treasury to pay off those debts. He was later arrested, indicted, and brought to trial. At trial he argued that he should be found not guilty because he fully intended to return all of the money. Is this a valid defense to embezzlement? Explain.

_____

_____

_____

_____

7. While sleepwalking in his dormitory one night, Stevens ran into Claymore, a classmate. Stevens knocked Claymore n down some stairs. Claymore wanted the police to arrest Stevens. Did the police comply with the request? Explain.

_____

_____

_____

_____

8. Morris offered the mayor of Shelby $10,000 to award Morris's firm a high-way contract. The mayor refused the bribe. When Morris was arrested, he claimed that he was innocent of the charge of bribery because the mayor never took the money. Was he correct? Explain.

_____

_____

_____

_____

9. Schmitt took a shortcut through Woodward's backyard. While passing by Woodward's living room, he saw a valuable camera on a table. Schmitt opened a window and used a long stick to lift the camera by its strap and haul it out the window. When charged with burglary, Schmitt argued that he had neither broken into nor entered the Woodward home. Therefore, he concluded that he could not be charged with burglary. Was he correct? Explain.

_____

_____

_____

_____

10. Magill was cleaning his .45 automatic revolver when it discharged and killed his friend. Magill claimed that he could not be charged with any crime because the killing was unintentional. Was he correct? Explain.

_____

_____

_____

_____

Chapter 6   Tort Law

Chapter Outline

6-1   Tort Law Defined

    A. A tort is _____
_____

    B. The primary purpose of tort law is to _____
_____
_____

    C. The doctrine of *respondeat superior* may impose tort liability on ___
_____
_____

    D. A duty is _____
_____

6-2   Intentional Torts

    A. Assault and Battery
        1. An assault occurs when_____
_____

        2. A battery occurs when_____
_____

    B. False imprisonment is _____
_____

    C. Defamation is _____
_____

    D. Disparagement is_____
_____

    E. Fraud is _____
_____

    F. Privacy can be violated in the following ways _____
_____
_____

    G. Intentional infliction of emotional distress requires _____
_____

    H. Misuse of legal procedure occurs when _____
_____

6-3 Negligence

  A. The elements of negligence are _____

     1. _____

     2. _____

     3. _____

     4. _____

  B. Defenses to negligence include _____

     1. _____

     2. _____

     3. _____

6-4 Strict Liability

  A. The doctrine of strict liability applies to ultrahazardous activities including

     1. _____

     2. _____

  B. Product liability extends to

     1. _____

     2. _____

     3. _____

6-5 Electronic Torts

  A. An electronic tort involves _____

  B. E-defamation is _____

  C. E-desparagement is _____

  D. E-invasion of privacy is _____

6-6 Remedies for Torts

  A. The Right to Damages _____

     1. Damages are _____

     2. Punitive damages are _____

  B. An injunction is _____

6-7 Tort Reform

  A. Survival statutes allow _____

  B. Wrongful death statutes preserve _____

Legal Concepts

For each statement, write **T** *in the answer column if the statement is true or* **F** *if the statement is false.*

Answer

1. A tort is a private wrong that injures another person's well-being, property or reputation.   1. _____
2. The primary purpose of tort law is to compensate the innocent victim.   2. _____
3. Employers can never be held liable for the torts of their employees.   3. _____
4. Assault and battery always occur together.   4. _____
5. Libel is defamation in a temporary form.   5. _____
6. The actual malice test applies only to public officials.   6. _____
7. Invasion of privacy occurs only when confidential records are revealed.   7. _____
8. The reasonable person test is a subjective test.   8. _____
9. Proximate cause is not a necessary element of negligence.   9. _____
10. Actual harm is a necessary element of negligence.   10. _____
11. Comparative negligence completely prevents recovery by the injured party.   11. _____
12. Assumption of the risk involves the voluntary exposure of the victim to a known risk.   12. _____
13. Strict liability is generally applied when the harm that results comes from an ultrahazardous activity.   13. _____
14. Damages cannot include compensation for lost wages.   14. _____
15. The rights of third parties affected by the death of the deceased are preserved by survival statutes.   15. _____

Language of the Law

Select the legal term that best matches each definition.

a. assault
b. battery
c. creating a false light
d. damages
e. defamation
f. false imprisonment
g. injunction
h. libel
i. negligence
j. punitive damages
k. tort
l. tortfeasor

Answer

1. A person who commits a tort   1. _____
2. Placing a victim in fear of immediate bodily harm   2. _____
3. Damages designed to punish   3. _____
4. An offensive or harmful unprivileged touching   4. _____
5. Defamation of a permanent form   5. _____
6. Preventing another party from moving about freely   6. _____

7. Any false statement that harms another's good name or reputation 7. _____

8. The part of tort law that is concerned with the compensation of accident victims 8. _____

9. A court order preventing the performance of an act 9. _____

10. Publication of information about a person that most people would see as unfavorable 10. _____

Applying the Law

1. Laura Mason, a waitress for the Highland Restaurant, was working in the dining room one morning when Fred Von Styne, a customer, said something that annoyed her. Without warning, Mason approached Von Styne, waving her tray menacingly. Before she could reach Von Styne, she was restrained by another waitress. When she was sued by Von Styne for assault, she argued that she could not possibly have committed an assault because she never touched Von Styne. Was she correct? Explain.

_____

_____

_____

_____

2. Roy Taggart owned and operated the Taggart Dress Shop. Taggart thought he saw Violet Damron place a blouse in her shopping bag. Taggart approached Damron and locked her in a closet for six hours. When Taggart was satisfied that Damron was innocent, he released her. Damron sued for false imprisonment. Did she have a case? Explain.

_____

_____

_____

_____

3. Addie Franklin worked as a nurse at the Riverside County Clinic. Franklin read the records of Karen Gromley, another nurse who worked at the clinic. The records revealed that Gromley was in the hospital suffering from a very serious illness. Concerned about Gromley's health, Franklin spread the news of Gromley's illness throughout the clinic. She also took up a collection to buy flowers. When Gromley threatened an invasion of privacy suit, Franklin argued that because of her good motive, the lawsuit would be groundless. Was she correct? Explain.

_____

_____

_____

_____

4. Willy Evans and Olaf Erickson did not get along as neighbors. Evans printed several false accusations about Erickson in a flier which he passed out in the neighborhood. As a result, Erickson was evicted from his apartment. What type of lawsuit, if any, could Erickson bring against Evans as a result? Explain.

_____

_____

_____

_____

5. Rick Gardner, the owner of a baseball stadium, was sued by Ted Fuller, a spectator injured by a foul ball hit during a game in Gardner's stadium. Gardner claimed that the lawsuit would not hold up as long as it could be shown that Fuller was aware of the risk of injuries from foul balls, which are associated with viewing baseball in a stadium. Was he correct? Explain.

_____

_____

_____

_____

6. While test driving her new motorcycle on an interstate highway, Giordano decided to take the bike up to 110 mph and try several tricky maneuvers in heavy traffic. As a result, she lost control of the bike and crashed into several automobiles and trucks, injured several people, and caused extensive damage to the vehicles. Giordano was sued by the victims. What test would be used to judge her conduct to determine whether she breached her duty to the other people on the interstate? Explain.

_____

_____

_____

_____

7. Charles Wilkinson purchased a hair dryer from the Frederickson Appliance Store. That afternoon she plugged it in and received a severe shock for which she was briefly hospitalized. An investigation revealed that the entire line of hair dryers had been manufactured based on a defective wiring diagram. Wilkinson sued the manufacturer, Milligan Electronics, Inc., and the seller, the Frederickson Appliance Store. Wilkinson argued that the hair dryer had been sold to her in a defective condition. Name and explain the legal theory that she was using.

_____

_____

_____

_____

8. Abrams recklessly drove his snowmobile down several city streets during a snowstorm. While doing so, he failed to see several pedestrians crossing the street and collided with them, injuring them seriously. Abrams argued that he had no duty to avoid hitting pedestrians who were in the street during the snowstorm. Was he correct? Explain.

_____

_____

_____

_____

9. Baker was playing with a neighbor's hunting rifle when it discharged accidentally. The bullet from the rifle hit Baker's front lawn, causing no damage to anyone or to the property. Baker said that he was not negligent in this incident. Was he correct? Explain.

_____

_____

_____

_____

10. Beatty invited Parsons on a boat ride out in Lake Erie. After several hours, Parsons told Beatty that she wanted to return to shore. Beatty refused and, despite continued protests from Parsons, kept her on the water for five more hours. Parsons sued Beatty for false imprisonment. Beatty argued that there was no false imprisonment because Parsons was not restrained or locked up. Was he correct? Explain.

_____

_____

_____

_____

Chapter 7   The Nature, Characteristics and Status of Contracts

Chapter Outline

7-1 The Basics of Contract Law

A. A contract is_____

_____

_____

B. The objective of contract law is _____

_____

_____

C. The three theories of contract law are _____

_____

_____

D. The six elements of a contract are

1.   _____

2.   _____

3.   _____

4.   _____

5.   _____

6.   _____

E. Article 2 of the UCC sets down_____

_____

_____

F. To be enforceable an agreement must_____

_____

G. Privity means_____

_____

7-2 Contractual Characteristics

A. Valid, void, voidable, and unenforceable contracts

1. A valid contract is_____

_____

_____

2. A void contract is _____

_____

_____

3. A voidable contract is _____

_____

_____

    4. An unenforceable contract is _____

_____

_____

B. Unilateral and bilateral contracts

    1. A unilateral contract is _____

_____

_____

    2. A bilateral contract is _____

_____

_____

C. Express and implied contracts

    1. An express contract is _____

_____

_____

    2. An implied-in-fact contract is _____

_____

_____

    3. An implied-in-law contract is _____

_____

_____

D. Informal and formal contracts

    1. An informal contract is _____

_____

_____

    2. A formal contract is _____

_____

_____

    3. A contract of record is _____

_____

_____

E. Executory and Executed Contracts _____

    1. An executory contract is _____

_____

    2. An executed contract is _____

_____

Legal Concepts

For each statement, write **T** *in the answer column if the statement is true or* **F** *if the statement is false.*   **Answer**

1. All contracts must be in writing to be enforceable.   1._____

2. A legally complete contract arises between two parties when at least four of the six elements of a contract are present.   2._____

3. Article 2 of the Uniform Commercial Code (UCC) sets down the rules that govern sale of goods contracts.   3._____

4. A general rule of contract law is that the parties to a contract must stand in privity to one another.   4._____

5. All contracts contain agreements but not all agreements are contracts.   5._____

6. A voidable contract has no legal effect whatsoever.   6._____

7. An unenforceable contract may have all of the elements of a complete contract and still may not be upheld by a court of law.   7._____

8. A unilateral contract comes into existence at the moment the initial promise is made.   8._____

9. An express contract is created by the actions or gestures of the parties involved in the transaction.   9._____

10. The quasi-contract concept cannot be applied when one party bestows a benefit on another party unnecessarily or through misconduct or negligence.   10._____

11. Any oral or written contract that is neither under seal nor a contract of record is considered an informal contract.   11._____

12. A formal contract differs from other contracts in that it has to be written, signed, witnessed, placed under the seal of the parties, and delivered.   12._____

13. All states still require the use of the seal in agreements related to the sale of real property.   13._____

14. Contracts of record are not true contracts because they are court created.   14._____

15. A contract can never be partly executory.   15._____

Language of the Law

Select the legal term that best matches each definition.

a. Bartering
b. breach of contract
c. contract
d. contract of record
e. executed contract
f. executory contract
g. express contract
h. implied-in-fact contract
i. implied-in-law contract
j. privity
k. unenforceable contract
l. unilateral contract
m. valid contract
n. voidable contract
o. void contract

Answer

1. A special type of formal contract having certain unique characteristics

1. _____

2. A contract that can be imposed by a court in a situation in which it can be proved that the parties did not create a written, an oral, or an implied-in-fact agreement

2. _____

3. A contract that has not yet been fully performed

3. _____

4. An agreement between two or more competent parties, based on mutual promises, to do or to refrain from doing some particular thing that is neither illegal nor impossible

4. _____

5. A condition that exists when both parties to a contract have a legally recognized interest in the subject of the contract

5. _____

6. A contract, the terms of which have been completely and satisfactorily carried out by both parties

6. _____

7. A contract that is legally binding

7. _____

8. An exchange of services and/or goods that are equal in value, rather than a payment of money

8. _____

9. The failure of one of the parties to a contract to do what he or she has previously agreed to do

9. _____

10. A contract that can be canceled by one of the parties

10. _____

Applying the Law

1. Appleton and Franks Furniture entered into a contract whereby Appleton agreed to purchase a bedroom set, a dining room table, a desk, and a home entertainment center from Franks. Later, when a dispute arose as to the interpretation of the terms of the contract, Appleton argued that they should consult Article 2 of the UCC. Was Appleton correct? Explain.

_____

_____

_____

_____

2. The National Library and Book Sellers Club of American (NLBSCA) entered into a contract with the Culver City Convention Center to hold the NLBSCA's annual convention in Culver City. Later, NLBSCA breached the contract and moved the convention to Hollywood. Gerard, who owned the Gerard Family Restaurant across from the Culver City Convention Center, wanted to bring a breach of contract suit against NLBSCA. Could Gerard bring such a suit? Explain.

_____

_____

_____

_____

3. Angela James was found unconscious at the side of the highway. She was taken to the emergency room of the Riverside County Clinic, where she was treated and released. When she was later billed for the treatment, she refused to pay. Did James have to pay anything to Riverside? Explain.

_____

_____

_____

_____

4. White purchased a set of antique clocks from Olsen, who promptly delivered the clocks. White agreed to send a check the next day. Olsen's part of the contract was executed upon delivery of the clocks. How would you characterize White's portion of the contract? Explain.

_____

_____

_____

_____

5. Raymonds watched as a crew from the Universal Pool Company spent a month installing a hot tub in his backyard. When presented with a bill, Raymonds refused to pay, claiming that he had never ordered a hot tub. When the foreman checked the work order, he found out that he and his crew were at the wrong house. Did Raymonds have to pay for the work? Explain.

_____

_____

_____

_____

6. Adler took his car to the E-Z Car Wash Company and arranged to have the car washed. Through a mix-up in the paperwork, Adler's car was washed and waxed. When Adler returned, he refused to pay for the wax job. E-Z argued that a court would order Adler to pay under the principle of quasi-contract. E-Z was incorrect. Why?

_____

_____

_____

_____

7. Carson and Forbes entered into an agreement in which Carson agreed to sell his VCR to Forbes. The two parties wrote all the terms of the contract on the back of an old envelope. They then both signed the agreement. When the time came to execute the contract, Forbes claimed he was not bound by the terms because the law required all contracts to be formally drawn up on preprinted documents. He was incorrect. Why?

_____

_____

_____

_____

8. Hume agreed to take his two younger brothers to the Super Bowl. When the time came to go to the game, Hume discovered that all the tickets had been sold two weeks prior to his original agreement with his brothers. When Hume told them that he could not get tickets, they told him that they were going to sue him. Hume told his brothers they could not sue him for failing to obtain the tickets. He was correct. Why?

_____

_____

_____

9. Watson promised to sell his guitar to Coates if Coates would give him $250 in return. Coates promised to bring the money to Watson in exchange for the guitar. When Coates showed up with the money the next day, Watson refused to turn over the guitar, arguing that promises alone, without action, cannot create a contract. Watson was incorrect. Why?

_____

_____

_____

10. Austin agreed to construct a restaurant for Dewey. Before construction began, a change in the zoning regulations made it illegal to open a restaurant on Dewey's property. Austin argued that the contract was still valid. He was incorrect. Why?

_____

_____

_____

Chapter 8   Offer and Acceptance

Chapter Outline

8-1 Requirements of an Offer

A. An offer is _____
_____
_____

B. Serious intent is determined by _____
_____
_____

C. No valid offer exists when_____
_____

D. An offer may be communicated by _____
_____

8-2 Acceptance of an Offer

A. Communication of acceptance may be either _____
_____
_____

B. To be unequivocal an acceptance must not _____
_____
_____

   1. The mirror image rule says _____
_____
_____

   2. A counter offer is _____
_____
_____

C. Under the UCC as long as there is a definite expression of
acceptance a contract will _____
_____
_____

8-3 Revocation of an Offer

Offers may be revoked by

A. _____
_____

B. _____
_____

C. _____
_____

D. _____

E. _____
_____

F. _____
_____

8-4 Option
Contracts

A. An option contract is _____
_____

B. Under the UCC, a firm offer is _____
_____

C. A lease option is _____
_____
_____

8-5 Offer and
Acceptance in
Electronic
Contract Law

A. An electronic contract is _____
_____

B. The E-Sign Act represents an effort to _____
_____
_____

C. The Uniform Electronic Transactions Act was written by the
NCCUSL to _____
_____
_____

D. The Uniform Computer Transactions Act covers _____
_____
_____

E. A "click-on" agreement is _____
_____
_____

Legal Concepts

For each statement, write **T** *in the answer column if the statement is true or* **F** *if*   **Answer**
the statement is false.

1. An offer made as an obvious joke is invalid.
    1. _____

2. Most courts require absolute definiteness of terms before validating an offer.
    2. _____

3. The UCC forbids the omission of any information in an offer.
    3. _____

4. An offer must be communicated to the offeree in order to be valid.   4. _____

5. Newspaper and magazine advertisements are always considered public offers.   5. _____

6. Bilateral contracts do not usually require communication of an expressed acceptance.   6. _____

7. Communication of acceptance of an offer must always be express.   7. _____

8. An acceptance made by an authorized means of communication becomes effective when the acceptance is received by the offeror.   8. _____

9. Under the mirror image rule, if an acceptance changes or qualifies the terms in the offer, it is not an acceptance.   9. _____

10. The UCC has altered the mirror image rule.   10. _____

11. The delivery of unordered merchandise through the mail is now considered an offer to sell.   11. _____

12. An offeree can force an offeror into a contract by remaining silent if the offeror initiated the silence condition.   12. _____

13. When no time limit is set, an offer remains open until it is expressly revoked by the offeror.   13. _____

14. Destruction of the subject matter related to an offer automatically revokes that offer.   14. _____

15. The UCC requires consideration when a merchant agrees in writing to hold an offer open.   15. _____

Language of the Law

Select the legal term that best matches each definition.

a. acceptance
b. cost-plus contract
c. current market price contract
d. firm offer
e. invitation to trade
f. lease option
g. offer
h. offeree
i. offeror
j. option contract
k. output contract
l. public offer
m. rejection
n. requirements contract
o. revocation

                                              Answer

1. An agreement that binds an offeror to a promise to hold an offer open for a predetermined or a reasonable length of time   1. _____

2. A proposal by one party to another indicating a willingness to enter into a contract   2. _____

3. An agreement in which prices of certain goods are determined by reference to the market price of the goods as of a specified date   3. _____

4. A contract in which one party agrees to sell to a second party all the goods that the first party makes in a given period of time   4. _____

5. The person to whom an offer is made   5. _____

6. An announcement published to reach many people for the purpose of creating interest and attracting responses

6. _____

7. A contract that permits a party to lease real property while at the same time holding an option to purchase that same property.

7. _____

8. The calling back of an offer by an offeror

8. _____

9. An offer made through the public media but intended for a specific person whose identity or address is unknown.

9. _____

10. The person who makes an offer

10. _____

Applying the Law

1. Bryce had been having difficulty with his motorcycle. When he took it in for repairs, Marshall, the mechanic, told Bryce that the repairs would cost $600. Bryce told Marshall that he was so sick of all the problems with the motorcycle that he would gladly trade it in for a skateboard. Could Marshall take Bryce's statement as a valid contract? Explain.

_____

_____

_____

_____

2. Crane sent a letter to Yancey that said, "I'd like to buy one of your paintings for between $500 and $1,000." Is this a valid offer? Explain.

_____

_____

_____

_____

3. When Seth Ingalls rented an office from Sally Thomas, Thomas agreed, as the landlord, to pay a fair share of the expenses in redecorating the office. After the project was completed, Thomas refused to pay any of the expenses. What error did Ingalls make in the initial negotiations? Explain.

_____

_____

_____

_____

4. Kennedy found an expensive wristwatch at the community swimming pool. From an engraving on the back of the watch, Kennedy determined that the watch belonged to Lodge. Kennedy returned the watch to Lodge. The next day Kennedy learned that Lodge had posted a reward of $45 for the return of the missing watch. Could Kennedy collect the reward? Explain.

_____

_____

_____

_____

5. Simons sent an e-mail to Hatcher offering to purchase Hatcher's hunting lodge for $100,000. Hatcher decided to sell the lodge and sent a letter by U.S. mail to Simons stating his decision. Hatcher, however, failed to address the envelope properly. This error delayed Simons receipt of the acceptance by five days. Before receiving the letter, Simons purchased another hunting lodge owned by Edwards. Hatcher claimed that Simons must also buy Hatcher's lodge because Simons's acceptance was valid when Hatcher mailed the letter. Hatcher was incorrect. Why?

_____

_____

_____

_____

6. The president of Rader Industries offered Kubach a job as human resources director. Kubach said she would take the job as long as the president agreed to grant her an annual $1,500 bonus each Christmas. The president refused to agree to the bonus. Kubach argued that the president had to agree because Kubach had already accepted the president's offer and had thus created a contract. Kubach was incorrect. Why?

_____

_____

_____

_____

7. Ludwig watched all day long as contractors from the Frazetta Cement Company laid a new driveway on his property. The contractors were actually at the wrong house and on the wrong street. When Frazetta later billed Ludwig, he refused to pay. Ludwig was incorrect in his refusal. Why?

_____

_____

_____

_____

8. Knight received a set of bathroom towels through the U.S. mail from a merchandising house in Casper, Wyoming. A letter sent with the towels told her she could either send the merchandising house $20 or return the set within fourteen days. Knight did neither. Instead, she kept the towels and used them in her bathroom. Knight was correct in keeping the towels. Why?

_____

_____

_____

_____

9. Russell wanted to sell several acres of land he owned near Rattlesnake Cliffs. He sent an e-mail to Flenner stating in part, "If I don't receive an answer from you by noon on February 28, I will take your silence as an acceptance." Flenner did not respond by noon on February 28. Flenner had the right to hold Russell to the agreement. Why?

_____

_____

_____

_____

10. Massie offered to sell Claypool some lakeshore property for $67,000. Claypool asked for time to consider the offer. Massie agreed to hold the offer open for one week in return for Claypool's payment of $25. The next day, Claypool told Massie that he had decided not to purchase the property. Claypool then asked for his money back. Massie refused to return the $25. Massie's refusal was correct. Why?

_____

_____

_____

_____

Chapter 9   Mutual Assent and Defective Agreement

Chapter Outline

9-1 Mutual Assent

    A. Mutual assent means _____

    _____

    _____

    _____

    B. A defective agreement can result from _____

    _____

    _____

    _____

9-2 Fraud and Misrepresentation

    A. Fraud in the inception occurs when _____

    _____

    _____

    B. Fraud in the inducement occurs when _____

    _____

    _____

    C. Active fraud occurs when _____

    _____

    _____

    D. Passive fraud occurs when_____

    _____

    _____

    E. Misrepresentation is_____

    _____

    _____

9-3 Mistake

    A. A unilateral mistake does not offer _____

    _____

    _____

    B. A mutual mistake allows _____

    _____

    _____

C. Mutual mistakes that are grounds for rescission are

1. _____

2. _____

3. _____

9-4　**Duress and Undue Influence**

A. Physical duress involves either _____

_____

_____

B. Economic duress consists of _____

_____

_____

C. Undue influence occurs when _____

_____

_____

Legal Concepts

For each statement, write **T** *in the answer column if the statement is true or* **F** *if the statement is false.*

Answer

1. Mutual assent evolves through the communication of an offer and an acceptance between the contracting parties.

1. _____

2. Fraud may arise either from a party's intentional false statement or from the concealment of material facts and conditions.

2. _____

3. The turning back of a car's odometer may be considered a perpetration of active fraud.

3. _____

4. The term *misrepresentation* is synonymous with fraud.

4. _____

5. Exaggerated arguments and opinions made by salespersons to induce customers to buy their products are considered perpetrations of fraud.

5. _____

6. Passive conduct that is intended to deceive is fraudulent.

6. _____

7. In both fraud and misrepresentation, the injured party is permitted to terminate the contract and sue for damages.

7. _____

8. A mistake of a material fact, when made by both contracting parties, is grounds for contract rescission.

8. _____

9. A unilateral mistake made by an innocent purchaser of goods gives that purchaser the right to return the goods and demand the return of any money already paid for them.

9. _____

10. Proof that the subject matter of an agreement had been destroyed before the agreement was made is grounds for rescission.

10. _____

11. A bilateral mistake as to the value of the subject matter of a contract will excuse performance of the agreement.

11. _____

12. Force or the threat of force, when used in the creation of contractual obligations, is grounds for repudiation of a contract.

13. Economic duress involves a threat to a person's employment or financial security that entices that person to agree to contract obligations.

14. Exposure to public ridicule might constitute economic duress.

15. To prove undue influence, a confidential relationship must be shown to have existed between the parties prior to the agreement in question.

12. _____

13. _____
14. _____

15. _____

Language of the Law

Select the legal term that best matches each definition.

a. active fraud
b. bilateral mistake
c. concealment
d. confidential relationship
e. duress

f. economic duress
g. emotional duress
h. fraud in the inception
i. fraud in the inducement
j. passive fraud

k. physical duress
l. rescission
m. sales puffery
n. undue influence
o. unilateral mistake

Answer

1. Actions or statements made by one contracting party intending to deceive the other contracting party

2. Excessive pressure used by the dominant party in a confidential relationship to persuade the weaker party to enter into a contract benefiting the dominant party

3. Threats of exposure to public ridicule

4. The type of fraud that results when one party tricks another party by lying about the actual nature of the contract

5. The deliberate nondisclosure or intentional disguise of material facts or conditions that, if known by a contracting party, would significantly affect that party's contractual decision

6. The type of fraud that results when one party lies about the terms of the agreement to trick the other party to enter the contract under false pretenses

7. A mistake made by both contracting parties

8. Inducing a party to assent to a contract through the use or threat of violence

9. Expressions considered to be persuasive but not allowing rescission on grounds of fraud or misrepresentation

10. A mistake involving only one of the contracting parties

1. _____

2. _____
3. _____

4. _____

5. _____

6. _____
7. _____

8. _____

9. _____
10. _____

Applying the Law

1. Evans agreed to sell his private plane to Boyd for $125,000. Unknown to either of them, the night before, the plane had been stolen and destroyed in an air crash. Could the agreement be rescinded? Explain.

_____

_____

_____

_____

2. Yardley purchased a gemstone from Hillier for $10. Both Yardley and Hillier believed that this was an accurate statement of the value of the gemstone. Yardley later had the stone assessed and discovered it was actually worth $1000. Hillier wants either the gemstone returned or a payment of $990 from Yardley. Why will Hillier fail on this request?

_____

_____

_____

_____

3. Williams entered into a contract in which she agreed to sell a cottage by Lake Holloway to Porter. Williams knew that the foundation of the house was cracked, even though the crack was not visible by ordinary inspection. Williams did not reveal the defect to Porter. The next time it rained, water leaked in through the crack and did severe damage to the basement of the cottage. Could Porter recover anything from Williams in a lawsuit? Explain.

_____

_____

_____

_____

4. Noble offered to sell a desk to Yardley for $500. Yardley believed that the desk was made of an expensive teak wood from India. Noble had said nothing about what the desk was made of. Later Yardley found out that the desk was made of pine. Could Yardley win a lawsuit against Noble? Explain.

_____

_____

_____

_____

5. Meecham signed a written contract to sell her house to Haley for $112,400. Unknown to either of them at the time of the agreement, the house had been destroyed by fire earlier that day. For what legal reason could Haley rescind the contract for the sale of the house?

_____

_____

_____

_____

6. Chandler entered into a contract to buy a lot of land from Boland, who knew that Chandler planned to build a factory on it. Later, Chandler learned that the zoning laws of the community would not allow a factory to be built on the property. Why couldn't Chandler rescind the contract to buy the lot from Boland?

_____

_____

_____

_____

7. Capriotti described a car that was being sold to Glenn as the best car ever built by General Motors, one that would pass any other car on the road when it was tuned up. Capriotti also maintained that Glenn could never equal its price in the used car market. Investigation proved all of Capriotti's statements to be false. Why couldn't Glenn recover damages on grounds of fraud?

_____

_____

_____

_____

8. Jamison signed a contract to sell her home based on the buyer's threat that failure to agree to sell would result in Jamison losing her position as credit manager with a firm where the buyer had close connections. Jamison later moved to have the agreement rescinded on grounds of duress. Why would Jamison succeed in repudiating the agreement?

_____

_____

_____

_____

9. Community Hardware Store sold Hawkins a ripsaw that they told him was a crosscut saw. Hawkins did not discover the mistake until he started using the saw two days later. Community Hardware refused to refund Hawkins's money or make an exchange. Why could Hawkins return the saw and recover the money paid?

_____

_____

_____

_____

10. Calvarese examined a car being sold by Milltown Motors. She observed that the tires had little remaining tread, that the car showed signs of accident-related damage, and that the car had recently been repainted to conceal the damage. The salesperson stated that the car had always received excellent care, had good tires, had the original paint, and had never been in an accident. Calvarese bought the car and later attempted to rescind the agreement on grounds of fraud. Why would she be unsuccessful in this attempt?

_____

_____

_____

_____

Chapter 10　　Contractual Capacity

Chapter Outline

10-1　Minors' Rights and Obligations

A. Minority describes a party who _____
_____
_____

B. When minors lie about their age, most states _____
_____
_____

10-2　Contractual Capacity of Minors

A. A minor's contract for necessaries is _____
_____
_____

B. Minors may not disaffirm the following contracts:
_____
_____
_____
_____

C. Ratification is _____
_____
_____

D. A minor may disaffirm an agreement _____
_____
_____

10-3　Other Capacity Problems

A. A contract made by someone who is mentally ill may be valid if
_____
_____
_____
_____

B. Persons declared by a court to be insane are _____
_____
_____
_____
_____

C. A contract agreed to by someone under the influence of alcohol or drugs is _____

_____

_____

_____

Legal Concepts

For each statement, write **T** *in the answer column if the statement is true or* **F** *if the statement is false.*

Answer

1. The presumption that anyone entering into a contractual relationship has the legal capacity to do so is rebuttable.

    1. _____

2. A person reaches legal age on the anniversary of his or her birth.

    2. _____

3. In most states, if a minor disaffirms a contract, the minor is entitled to a return of everything paid to the other party of the contract.

    3. _____

4. Necessaries, as related to minors' contracts, vary with the financial and social status of each particular minor.

    4. _____

5. In all states, minors who are married may not disaffirm their contracts.

    5. _____

6. Continuing to accept the benefits of a contract after having reached majority affirms or ratifies an otherwise voidable contract.

    6. _____

7. In most cases, parents are not liable for contracts executed by their minor children unless the parents have cosigned a contract.

    7. _____

8. Minors may, at their option, disaffirm a valid marriage.

    8. _____

9. After reaching legal age, adults may not disaffirm an agreement made during minority.

    9. _____

10. A person who has a voidable title to personal property may transfer a valid title to an innocent purchaser of that property.

    10. _____

11. All agreements made by people with mental impairments are void.

    11. _____

12. A minor who has sold real estate to someone who later sells it to an innocent third party may, on reaching adulthood, disaffirm and recover the real property.

    12. _____

13. Persons declared to be legally insane are denied the right to enter into contracts.

    13. _____

14. Minors may, at their option, disaffirm a valid contract for enlistment in the armed forces.

    14. _____

15. A contract agreed to by a person under the influence of alcohol may be voidable if the intoxicated party has lost the ability to comprehend the obligations under the contract.

    15. _____

Language of the Law

Select the legal term that best matches each definition.

a. abandoned
b. affirmance
c. capacity
d. disaffirm
e. emancipated
f. majority
g. minority
h. necessaries
i. ratification
j. rebuttable presumption
k. voidable

Answer

1. Freed from observing the laws regulating rights and obligations of minors' contracts

1. _____

2. The term that describes persons who have not yet reached majority

2. _____

3. Goods and services that are essential to a minor's health and welfare

3. _____

4. To show by a statement or act the intent not to live up to a voidable contract

4. _____

5. The term that describes a person who has reached adulthood

5. _____

6. The legal ability to enter into a contractual relationship

6. _____

7. The act of giving up a legal protection

7. _____

8. A legal assumption that can be disputed

8. _____

9. A promise or an act by a person reaching the age of majority that makes an agreement made during minority valid rather than voidable (select two answers)

9. _____

10. Title received by anyone buying something from a minor

10. _____

Applying the Law

1. Urchek used all of the money she received on her seventeenth birthday to purchase a complete new wardrobe from Spencer Department Store. After a week of storing the clothes in her closet, she saw a new iPod that she wanted. She returned the clothes to Spencer and demanded her money back. Must Spencer honor her request? Explain.

_____

_____

_____

_____

2. Boterus, a minor, bought a snowmobile from the Redy-2-Drive Used Snowmobile lot. The next day he accidentally ran the snowmobile into a tree and seriously damaged the vehicle. Boterus transported the damaged vehicle to Redy-2-Drive and demanded a return of his money. Must Redy-2-Drive comply with his request? Explain.

---

3. One week before her eighteenth birthday, Martha Cedric bought a used motorcycle from Hugson Motors. Cedric gave Hugson a down payment of $500 and agreed to pay Hugson $175 per month until the motorcycle was paid for. One month later, Cedric made her first payment to Hugson. The next day she tried to get out of the contract claiming that she was a minor when she entered the contract. Was the contract voidable by Cedric? Explain.

---

4. Nadir was declared incompetent by the court. The court appointed Berringer to serve as her guardian. One day Nadir wandered off and took a cab to the Jerard Department Store where she purchased a room full of furniture for $4,000. Will either Nadir or Berringer be required to pay for the furniture if Berringer decided that Nadir should not have made the purchase? Explain.

---

5. Two days before his eighteenth birthday, Lopez paid cash to purchase a new laptop from Platonic Office Supplies, Inc. Two days after his 18th birthday, he tried to Return it to Platonic. The manager of the Platonic store said that she did not have to accept the laptop because Lopez was no longer a minor. Was she correct? Explain.

---

6. Seventeen-year-old Adams signed a contract for a new car. Included in the contract was this statement: "I attest to the fact that at the time of signing this agreement I have reached age eighteen." Adams paid a small down payment and used the car for long trips during the following month. He later proposed to disaffirm the agreement. Why would Adams be permitted to avoid the contract and have no further responsibility to the seller?

_____

_____

_____

_____

7. Burell, a minor, sold certain property to Noyes at a reasonable price. Two years after reaching his majority, Burell demanded the return of his property and offered to return the money received for it. Noyes refused. Why couldn't Burell recover the property sold to Noyes?

_____

_____

_____

_____

8. Shockley, a wealthy sixteen-year-old orphan, ordered his tailor to make him a warm winter coat at a cost of $2225. When his coat was ready, Shockley informed the tailor that he had changed his mind and was voiding their agreement. Why could the tailor force Shockley to pay for the coat, even though Shockley had not yet reached his majority?

_____

_____

_____

_____

9. Turner agreed while intoxicated to sell his diamond ring, worth $350, to Murton for $50. The next day Turner changed his mind and refused to carry out the agreement. Murton brought suit against Turner for damages. Why would Murton be unsuccessful in this suit?

_____

_____

_____

_____

10. Rubin was known to neighbors and friends as being mentally incompetent. The state had never declared her insane because no one had ever been endangered by her actions. Teen Shop agreed to sell Rubin a coat. The shop did not recognize her lack of reasoning powers. The coat was a necessity. Why could Rubin be held liable for the cost of the coat?

_____

_____

_____

_____

Chapter 11   Consideration

Chapter Outline

11-1 **Requirements of Consideration**

A. Consideration consists of_____

_____

_____

_____

B. A detriment is any of the following:

  1. _____

  2. _____

  3. _____

C. Consideration involves the following characteristics:

  1. _____

_____

  2. _____

_____

_____

  3. _____

_____

11-2 **Types of Consideration**

A. The shift from a barter to a cash economy occurred when _____

_____

_____

_____

B. Before money was accepted as a medium of exchange consideration consisted of _____

_____

_____

C. A promise not to sue is called _____

_____

_____

D. A contemporary approach to enforcing a charitable pledge is to use either _____

_____

_____

11-3	**Problems with Consideration**	A.	A disputed amount is _____ _____ _____
		B.	An undisputed amount is _____ _____ _____ _____

11-4	**Agreements Without Consideration**	A.	Typical agreements that are enforceable without consideration include _____ _____ _____ _____
		B.	Agreements that the court will not enforce because they lack consideration include _____ _____ _____ _____

Legal Concepts

For each statement, write **T** *in the answer column if the statement is true or* **F** *if the statement is false.*

Answer

1. Consideration consists of a mutual exchange of benefits and sacrifices between contracting parties.

1. _____

2. The law will not enforce an agreement that has not been bargained for.

2. _____

3. Refraining from doing that which one has a legal right to do is valid consideration.

3. _____

4. The benefits and detriments exchanged as consideration must be legal.

4. _____

5. The concept of bargaining means that one person gains something and the other person loses something.

5. _____

6. The courts have held that barter agreements contain no valid consideration.

6. _____

7. When the right to sue exists, a promise not to sue is enforceable when supported by consideration.

7. _____

8. A pledge of money to a charitable institution is unenforceable because the charity gives no consideration.

8. _____

9. The courts will entertain arguments based on accord and satisfaction even in trivial and superficial disputes.

9. _____

10. When accepted by a creditor, a partial payment in lieu of full payment will cancel an undisputed debt. 10. _____

11. In some states, a seal gives a written contract the presumption of consideration. 11. _____

12. Debtors may revive and reaffirm debts barred by the statutes of limitations without the necessity of new consideration. 12. _____

13. A promise to give someone a gift at some future time is enforceable with no consideration. 13. _____

14. Past consideration makes an agreement binding. 14. _____

15. A promise to carry out an act that one is already obligated to do by law or contract is valid consideration to support a contract. 15. _____

Language of the Law

Select the legal term that best matches each definition.

a. accord
b. accord and satisfaction
c. bargained-for exchange
d. consideration
e. detriment

f. disputed amount
g. estoppel
h. forbearance
i. option
j. past consideration

k. preexisting duty
l. release
m. statutes of limitation
n. unconscionable
o. undisputed amount

Answer

1. Refraining from doing something that one has a legal right to do 1. _____

2. A court's opinion that a ridiculously inadequate amount of consideration is involved in a contract 2. _____

3. The giving of consideration to support an offeror's promise to hold an offer open for a reasonable length of time 3. _____

4. Statutes that specify the time period within which action on a contract must begin 4. _____

5. Doing something that one has a legal right not to do 5. _____

6. The implied or expressed acceptance by a creditor of less than the amount owed by a debtor 6. _____

7. A promise to do something that one is already obligated to do by law or by some other process or agreement 7. _____

8. A doctrine that denies to a complaining party rights that are shown to be the cause of that party's own injury 8. _____

9. A promise of consideration made to a party after that party has already performed an act for the benefit of the promisor 9. _____

10. The exchange of benefits and sacrifices by contracting parties that creates a binding agreement 10. _____

Applying the Law

1. Andrews promised to purchase a new tennis racquet from Raymonds for $150. Raymonds agreed to sell it for that price. Later, Andrews tried to rescind the transaction by arguing that she had not yet paid the consideration to Raymonds. Did the court agree with Andrews? Explain.

_____

_____

_____

_____

2. Wollers agreed to sell a stolen car to Licten. Licten failed to live up to his part of the deal. Does Wollers have a legitimate cause of action against Licten? Explain.

_____

_____

_____

_____

3. Quentin ran a stop sign and crashed into a car driven by Holland. After surveying the damage to both vehicles, they agreed that Holland would secure an estimate for repairs. Holland presented an estimate to Quentin for $1,289 in repairs. Quentin agreed to pay this amount but only if Holland agreed to sign a promise not to sue Quentin. Would this agreement not to sue be binding? Explain.

_____

_____

_____

_____

4. Sellars agreed to pay her son, Ken, $1,000 if he agreed not to smoke cigarettes for one year. At the end of the year, Ken asked for the $1,000. His mother refused to pay him the money, arguing that the abstinence had been to his benefit and could not, therefore, be valid consideration in a contract. Was Sellars correct? Explain.

_____

_____

_____

_____

5. When the Fire Department arrived at the Realistic Electronics Store to fight a fire in the warehouse, Henderson, the fire chief, said that his men would agree to fight the fire if Sutton, the owner of Realistic, paid them $100 each. Sutton agreed. Sutton later refused to pay. Did the chief have a valid cause of action against Sutton? Explain.

_____

_____

_____

_____

6. Harris had a flat tire at the side of the road leading into Butler. Jenkins stopped and helped Harris. As Harris drove away, he told Jenkins that he would send her $10 next week to pay her for her help in fixing his disabled vehicle. Was this agreement binding on Harris? Explain.

_____

_____

_____

_____

7. Zigmont purchased 100 gallons of gasoline from Oakwood Service Station at a rate of one dollar per gallon. Zigmont later learned that all other service stations in the city charged only 90 cents per gallon. Zigmont sent a check to Oakwood for $90 with the notation, "In full payment for the 100 gallons of gasoline purchased from your station." Oakwood deposited the check. Why could Oakwood still demand the $10 balance on Zigmont's bill?

_____

_____

_____

_____

8. Dr. Saltzer performed an operation on Hartmann. Hartmann received a bill for $1,500 instead of for the $500 the surgeon had led him to expect. Hartmann was angered and sent Saltzer a check for $500, writing on the back "In full payment for all professional services." The doctor cashed the check, indorsing it below Hartmann's notation. Why did the doctor have no recourse against Hartmann for the balance of $1,000?

_____

_____

_____

_____

9. Sanders assisted two elderly women whose car was stranded in a snowbank during a blizzard. More than an hour of work was required to get the car back on the highway. "Young man, we appreciate your kindness," the women said. "We promise that we will mail you a check for $25 for your work and time." Why couldn't Sanders enforce this promise if the check is not sent?

_____

_____

_____

_____

10. Dukes pledged $400 to a church that was planning to install a new organ. When the work was finished, she refused to honor the pledge. Dukes argued that since she had received no benefit, there was no consideration to support her pledge. Why could she be sued for the $400?

_____

_____

_____

_____

Chapter 12   Legality

Chapter Outline

12-1   Agreements to Engage in Unlawful Activity

    A. According to the law an agreement to commit a tort is_____
_____
_____
_____

    B. The law says that an agreement to commit a crime is_____
_____
_____
_____

    C. Some activities that are illegal by statute are:

        1. _____
        _____

        2. _____
        _____

        3. _____
        _____

        4. _____
        _____

        5. _____
        _____

12-2   Agreements Contrary to Public Policy

    A. Agreements to obstruct justice include _____
_____
_____

    B. Agreements interfering with public service include _____
_____
_____

    C. An agreement to defraud a creditor is _____
_____
_____
_____

D. An exculpatory agreement is _____

_____

_____

_____

E. An agreement in restraint of trade is _____

_____

_____

_____

12-3 Consequences of Illegality

A. Parties to a contract are said to be *in pari delicto* when _____

_____

_____

_____

B. If the legal part of a contract can be separated from the illegal part, the court will _____

_____

_____

_____

Legal Concepts

For each statement, write **T** *in the answer column if the statement is true or* **F** *if the statement is false.*

		Answer
1.	The law will not honor an agreement to commit a crime.	**1.** _____
2.	An agreement to commit a tort would be valid in the eyes of the law.	**2.** _____
3.	Wagering agreements are not affected by statutory law.	**3.** _____
4.	Businesses and professions are licensed solely as a means of collecting additional taxes for public use.	**4.** _____
5.	Contracts entered into on Sunday are invalid in all fifty states.	**5.** _____
6.	The enforcement of "blue laws" varies widely from state to state, county to county, and village to village.	**6.** _____
7.	Agreements made with the intent of suppressing competition or fixing prices are illegal restraints of trade and therefore void.	**7.** _____
8.	Any action that tends to harm the health, safety, welfare, or morals of the public is said to violate public policy.	**8.** _____
9.	An agreement to give false testimony at a trial is enforceable.	**9.** _____
10.	An agreement that tends to interfere with the service and proper performance of a public official is void as contrary to public policy.	**10.** _____
11.	Agreements that tend to weaken the rights of creditors are void.	**11.** _____

12. The law looks with disfavor on agreements that allow parties to escape liability for their own wrongdoing.　　12. _____

13. Exculpatory clauses, when part of an otherwise valid and legal agreement, ordinarily are enforceable as a matter of public policy.　　13. _____

14. Restrictive employment covenants must be reasonable in the type of work prohibited, the length of time involved, and the geographical area covered.　　14. _____

15. The rule of *in pari delicto* applies to agreements in which both parties are equally wrong and equally at fault.　　15. _____

Language of the Law

Select the legal term that best matches each definition.

a. Blue laws
b. conspiracy
c. contributory copyright Infringement
d. copyright
e. exculpatory cause
f. fair use
g. *in pari delicto*
h. local option
i. nondisclosure agreement
j. public policy
k. restraint of trade
l. restrictive covenant
m. usury

Answer

1. A privilege designed to protect rights that attach to artistic, literary, and musical works　　1. _____

2. A copyright exception granted for criticism, comment, reporting, teaching, scholarship, and research　　2. _____

3. A limitation on the full exercise of doing business with others　　3. _____

4. A clause in a business agreement that restricts the seller from entering the same type of business　　4. _____

5. An agreement requiring an employee to promise not to reveal confidential trade secrets　　5. _____

6. In equal fault　　6. _____

7. A device used in the attempt to escape liability　　7. _____

8. State laws that either limit or prohibit commercial transactions and certain other activities on Sunday　　8. _____

9. The general legal principle that says no one should be permitted to do anything that injures the public at large　　9. _____

10. Interest charged in excess of the rate permitted by state law　　10. _____

Applying the Law

1. Leach's video rental shop was not doing well because another video shop in the same community rented DVDs cheaper rate. Leach offered to pay Brazleton $2,000 if Brazleton would break into the competitor's shop and destroy the competitor's DVDs Brazleton agreed to do so but failed to carry out the transaction. Can Leach enforce the agreement? Why or why not?

_____

_____

_____

_____

2. Graf borrowed $1,000 from Steele and agreed to pay Steele $25 per day in interest until the loan was paid back. Why was the loan agreement illegal and void?

_____

_____

_____

_____

3. Bard entered into a contract with Kirsh to buy fishing equipment for $75, a boat for $300, and a machine gun for $500. Machine gun sales were illegal in that state. Bard later breached the contract. Will the court enforce the contract? Explain.

_____

_____

_____

_____

4. Metcalf, a ninety-one year-old widow, signed a contract to have vinyl siding placed on her bungalow for $150,000. On what grounds could Metcalf void the contract?

_____

_____

_____

_____

5. Dugan was an Air Force pilot but had never received a civilian pilot's license. Raskob hired him to fly a twin-engine aircraft from Denver to Detroit for $500 and expenses. Raskob refused to pay Dugan when Dugan landed in Detroit. Can Dugan enforce the contract? Explain.

_____

_____

_____

_____

6. Klein sold a restaurant to Goff for $50,000. As part of the agreement, Klein promised not to open another restaurant business for ten years within a 50-mile radius of the one sold. Seven years later, Klein opened a restaurant 30 miles away. Could Goff enforce the agreement? Explain.

_____

_____

_____

_____

7. Roberts specialized in chemical research for Hughes Chemical Company. Roberts had access to all secret materials that had resulted from research in this area by the company over a ten-year period. In her employment contract, Roberts had agreed not to accept employment with a competing firm for five years after the Hughes contract expired. Was this employment contract an illegal restraint of trade? Why or why not?

_____

_____

_____

_____

8. Fairton witnessed an accident at the corner of Broad and Chestnut streets. One of the drivers offered him $200 cash if he would disappear and not claim to be a witness. He accepted the $200. Three days later, Fairton offered testimony to the police department about what had happened. Could Fairton be sued for breach of the agreement with the driver? Explain.

_____

_____

_____

_____

9. Hines and O'Neal operated separate computer repair shops in Center County. These shops were the only ones offering repair service. Hines and O'Neal agreed on new and higher rates that each would charge for work done. Would this agreement be enforceable if O'Neal were to offer old rates and advertise for additional customers on the basis of the lower prices? Why or why not?

_____

_____

_____

_____

10. Gutierrez, a city building inspector and engineer, agreed to approve improper concrete work that had been done on the Hightower Building. Owners of the building promised to appoint Gutierrez to the position of building manager in return for the favors extended by the inspector. The Hightower Building's owners failed to carry out their agreement with Gutierrez. Could she recover damages for their breach of this agreement? Explain.

_____

_____

_____

_____

Chapter 13   Written Contracts

Chapter Outline

13-1   **The Statute of Frauds**

A. Contracts that must be in writing to be enforceable are

1. _____
2. _____
3. _____
4. _____
5. _____
6. _____

B. A written memorandum should contain the following elements:

1. _____
2. _____
3. _____
4. _____
5. _____

13-2   **Legal Rules for Written Contracts**

A. The standard construction rule says _____
_____
_____

B. The parol evidence rule says _____
_____
_____

C. Under the best evidence rule, courts will accept only_____
_____
_____
_____

D. The equal dignities rule provides that _____
_____
_____

13-3   **Formalities of Construction**

A. Written agreements should be, but need not be_____
_____

B. Witnesses are required in _____
_____
_____

C. Today's seal is usually nothing more than _____

_____

_____

13-4   Electronic Commerce

A. A digital signature is _____

_____

_____

B. The four most important electronic commerce statutes are _____

_____

_____

_____

_____

Legal Concepts

For each statement, write **T** *in the answer column if the statement is true or* **F** *if the statement is false.*   **Answer**

1. Most contracts must be in writing to be enforceable.   1. _____

2. If the terms of a contract make it impossible to complete the contract within six months, the contract must be in writing.   2. _____

3. Contracts for the sale of land valued at less than $500 may be either oral or written.   3. _____

4. Contracts for the transfer or sale of any interest in land do not necessarily have to be in writing.   4. _____

5. When a person relies on an owner's oral promise to sell him or her real estate and then makes improvements on the property, the court will uphold the agreement.   5. _____

6. Contracts for the sale of goods must be in writing when the property price is $500 or less.   6. _____

7. Under international law (CISG), contracts for the sale of goods need not be in writing.   7. _____

8. A promise to answer for and pay someone else's debts does not have to be in writing.   8. _____

9. Agreements in consideration of marriage must be in writing, but the marriage contract itself need not be.   9. _____

10. To satisfy the Statute of Frauds, a memorandum need not identify both parties to be obligated under the contract.   10. _____

11. On a memorandum, the only signature needed to satisfy the Statute of Frauds is that of the party sought to be bound to the agreement.   11. _____

12. Evidence of oral statements made before the signing of a written agreement is usually admissible in court to change the terms of the written agreement.   12. _____

13. The courts, under the best evidence rule, will accept only the original of a writing and not a copy.   13. _____

14. Any mark that the signer intends to be a signature will be the legal signature of that person.

15. The equal dignities rule provides that when someone appoints an agent to negotiate an agreement that must be in writing, the appointment of the agent may be oral.

14. _____

15. _____

Language of the Law

Select the legal term that best matches each definition.

a. administrator
b. best evidence rule
c. equal dignities rule
d. guaranty of payment

e. guarantor
f. memorandum
g. obligee
h. obligor

i. parol evidence rule
j. prenuptial agreement
k. primary objective test
l. Statute of Frauds

Answer

1. An agreement in which two people planning to marry agree to change the property rights that usually arise in marriage

2. Evidence of oral statements made before signing a written agreement is usually not admissable in court to contradict or change the terms of a written agreement

3. Courts accept as evidence only the original of a writing

4. When an agent is appointed to negotiate an agreement that must itself be in writing, the appointment of the agent must also be in writing

5. A person appointed to carry out the provisions of a will when an executor cannot do so

6. British law, now incorporated in state statutes, specifying the agreements that must be in writing to be enforceable

7. A person who owes an original debt

8. A guaranty of payment made to secure a benefit for the guarantor

9. A person who agrees to pay the debt of another

10. A promise to pay another person's debt

1. _____

2. _____

3. _____

4. _____

5. _____

6. _____

7. _____

8. _____

9. _____

10. _____

Applying the Law

1. A week before they were married, Stein and Warren agreed orally that if their marriage did not last, Stein would receive the real estate they owned and Warren would receive the remainder of their property. Would this agreement be upheld by the court? Explain.

_____

_____

_____

_____

2. Ortez orally agreed to sell her computer printer to Wood for $350. She later tried to back out of the deal on the grounds that the oral agreement was unenforceable. Would a court hold Ortez to her promise? Why or why not?

_____

_____

_____

_____

3. In a lawsuit against Feingold, Penders attempted to introduce into evidence a photocopy of a contract the parties had signed. Was the copy allowed into evidence by the court? Explain.

_____

_____

_____

_____

4. Gretto was named administrator of Hall's estate. In defense of Hall's widow, who was threatened with suit unless certain bills of Hall's were paid immediately, Gretto said, "Leave my sister-in-law be. You'll get your money. If things get worse, I'll pay the bills myself." In consideration of this promise, the creditors withdrew their threats. If the accounts are not settled by the estate, could Gretto be charged for the creditors' losses? Why or why not?

_____

_____

_____

_____

5. Zelinski entered into an oral agreement appointing Farm Realty Company as his agent to sign a contract to sell Zelinski's 125-acre farm and buildings for $225,000. Farm Realty signed a contract with a buyer who gave a down payment. Zelinski personally secured another buyer who agreed to pay $250,000 for the property. Was Zelinski obliged to the contract made for him by Farm Realty Company? Explain.

_____

_____

_____

_____

6. O'Brien was interviewed for a job on Thursday. The interview was successful, and she agreed orally to start working the following Monday, to be employed from that day, Monday, for one year thereafter. Three weeks after starting the job, O'Brien was fired without cause and replaced by the employer's niece. Would O'Brien be successful in an action brought against the employer for damages? Explain.

_____

_____

_____

_____

7. Venturo, a former professional football player, suffered from a crippling disease and lost the use of his right arm. He was offered the job of television announcer for the season of games in his former league. The contract requires Venturo's signature, which he was not able to affix to the contract. What other procedures could be taken to ensure that Venturo's signature would be affixed to the contract?

_____

_____

_____

_____

8. Archer wrote to Katz, offering to sell a diamond ring to Katz for $7,800. Katz replied by return mail, accepting the offer. Archer discovered that the ring would bring more money at an auction and sought to cancel the agreement, arguing that the Statute of Frauds required personal property sales above $500 to be in writing. Could Katz enforce the agreement? Why or why not?

_____

_____

_____

_____

9. LeBlanc purchased four tires from Central Tire Company. Aparicio, her boyfriend, telephoned Central Tire to promise that if LeBlanc failed to honor her bill, he would pay it himself. On this basis, Central Tire proceeded to mount the tires on LeBlanc's car. She did not honor her bill. Could Aparicio be held liable on his telephoned promise to pay LeBlanc's bill? Explain.

_____

_____

_____

_____

10. Jeness signed a contract agreeing to purchase a used van for $2,080. The sales representative of Guarantee Motors explained that the van would be guaranteed for six months for all labor and repairs. The written contract contained nothing about the warranty. Jeness had severe and expensive difficulties with the van and returned the vehicle to Guarantee Motors for the repairs promised under the agreement with the firm's representative. Would Jeness's demands for performance of the guarantee be upheld? Why or why not?

_____
_____
_____
_____

Chapter 14   Third Parties in Contract Law

Chapter Outline

14-1 **Contracts and Third Parties**

  A. The most frequently recognized intended beneficiaries are

  1. _____

  2. _____

  3. _____

  B. An incidental beneficiary is: _____

  _____

  _____

  _____

14-2 **Assignment of Contracts**

  A. Rights are assigned and duties are _____

  _____

  B. The parties to an assignment are

  1. _____

  2. _____

  3. _____

  C. To create an assignment, consideration is_____

  _____

  _____

  _____

  _____

  D. Assignments may be accomplished through_____

  _____

  _____

  _____

  _____

14-3 **Assignment Rights, Duties and Restrictions**

  A. The rights and duties of an assignee are _____

  _____

  _____

  _____

  _____

A. A party may not delegate duties that _____

_____

_____

C. Assignments, in special situations, may be restricted by _____

_____

_____

_____

D. A novation is _____

_____

_____

_____

Legal Concepts

For each statement, write **T** *in the answer column if the statement is true or* **F** *if the statement is false.*   **Answer**

1. A creditor beneficiary is an outside third party who owes a continuing debt of obligation to one of the contracting parties.   **1.** _____

2. Donee beneficiaries have no legal grounds to bring suit for acts promised by contracting parties.   **2.** _____

3. Incidental beneficiaries have legal grounds for enforcing the contract made by those in privity of contract.   **3.** _____

4. When no consideration is given for an assignment, creditors of the assignor may have the assignment rescinded on the grounds that it is a fraudulent conveyance.   **4.** _____

5. Assignments may be accomplished through written, oral, or implied agreements between the assignor and the assignee.   **5.** _____

6. The law permits the assignment of all types of valid and enforceable executory contracts.   **6.** _____

7. In an assignment, "the assignee steps into the shoes of the assignor."   **7.** _____

8. The assignor is obligated to any express and implied warranties that serve to protect either the assignee or the obligor.   **8.** _____

9. There is an implied warranty that duties owed to an obligor will be carried out in a complete and satisfactory manner by an assignee.   **9.** _____

10. One may not delegate duties that are of a personal or professional nature.   **10.** _____

11. Rights are generally delegated and duties are generally assigned.   **11.** _____

12. The right of assignment may be restricted by agreement of the parties.   **12.** _____

13. Members of the armed forces may assign their pay to whomever they wish.   **13.** _____

14. The assignor, rather than the assignee, is required to notify the obligor of an assignment.   **14.** _____

15. Novations differ from assignments in that a novation is an entirely new agreement.   **15.** _____

Language of the Law

Select the legal term that best matches each definition.

a. assignee
b. assignment
c. assignor
d. beneficiary
e. creditor beneficiary

f. delegation
g. donee beneficiary
h. incidental beneficiary
i. insurance beneficiary
j. intended beneficiary

k. novation
l. obligor
m. outside party
n. third party
o. warranty

Answer

1. A beneficiary in whose favor a contract is made

1. _____

2. A third party who does not provide any consideration for benefits received and who does not owe the contracting parties any legal duties

2. _____

3. A transfer of a contract right

3. _____

4. The remaining party to the original agreement after an assignment takes place

4. _____

5. A transfer of a contract duty

5. _____

6. Someone who could benefit indirectly from a contract performance but whose benefit was not of concern when the contract was made; this person cannot sue to recover any benefits

6. _____

7. One who transfers contract rights to another

7. _____

8. A third party who receives benefits from a contract made by others

8. _____

9. The creation of a new contract to replace one in which the performance has not yet commenced or has been only partly executed

9. _____

10. A promise, statement, or other representation that an item has certain qualities

10. _____

Applying the Law

1. Davis owed Prue $250. Prue told Davis to give the money to Prue's nephew, Weeks, as a college graduation present from Prue. Before the money was paid, however, Prue canceled the assignment and told Davis to pay Prue the money instead. Would Weeks have a cause of action against Prue? Explain.

_____

_____

_____

_____

2. Adams was owed $20,000 by Hull. In payment for a yacht, Adams assigned the right to receive the $20,000 to Christo. Christo did not notify Hull of the assignment, and Hull paid the $20,000 to Adams. Adams went bankrupt. Would Christo lose the $20,000? Why or why not?

_____

_____

_____

_____

3. Foss entered into a contract to sell 1,000 cases of computer paper to Morris for $5,000. Later, Foss delegated to Zito the task of selling the paper to Morris. Foss also assigned Zito the right to receive the $5,000. Morris did not agree to either the delegation or the assignment. Foss claimed that this was a novation. Was Foss correct? Explain.

_____

_____

_____

_____

4. Dr. Gravers, an obstetrician, accepted O'Leary as a patient during the period of her pregnancy and delivery. Eight months later, Gravers informed O'Leary that he planned to take a vacation in Bermuda. Without O'Leary's permission, Gravers assigned the case to Dr. Harrison, an equally reputable and skillful obstetrician. O'Leary claimed that she didn't have to go to the new doctor. Was O'Leary correct?

_____

_____

_____

_____

5. Sung paid premiums on a contract of fire insurance in which Rawlins, a partner, was named as beneficiary in event of a fire loss. The insurer agreed to those terms, but when a fire loss arose, the company refused to pay the amount of the proved loss to the named beneficiary, claiming that the beneficiary had not given any consideration in return for this unearned benefit. Was the insurance company liable to Sung's named beneficiary? Why or why not?

_____

_____

_____

_____

6. The Bay Bridge Authority contracted with Salakas Painting Contractors for the repainting of all steelwork on the bridge. It was agreed that Salakas would use Continental Paint, a particular brand, on the job. It was later discovered that paint manufactured by another firm had been used in painting the bridge. Could Continental Paint Company recover damages from Salakas for failure to use its paint as provided in the contract with Bay Bridge Authority? Why or why not?

_____

_____

_____

_____

7. Jenkins entered into a written contract to buy a parcel of real estate from Harcourt for $125,000. Before the contract was carried out, Jenkins assigned his rights under the contract to Campbell through a telephone conversation. Was the assignment enforceable? Why or why not?

_____

_____

_____

_____

8. In the above case, would the assignment to Campbell have been enforceable had the written contract between Jenkins and Harcourt stated, "Neither party may assign this contract without the express permission of the other party thereto"? Why or why not?

_____

_____

_____

_____

9. Myette agreed to paint Ortega's house for $2,000, provided that Ortega would pay the money to Myette's daughter. If Myette painted the house and Ortega failed to pay the $2,000, would Myette's daughter have the right to bring suit? Why or why not?

_____

_____

_____

_____

10. Carter hired Wintersteen, a well-known artist, to paint her portrait. Due to an overload of work, Wintersteen delegated the task of painting Carter's portrait to Regan, a budding art student. Was Carter bound to the delegation? Why or why not?

_____

_____

_____

_____

Chapter 15   Discharge and Remedies

Chapter Outline

15-1   **Discharge by Performance**

    A. When time for performance is not stated in a contract, the contract must be performed_____

_____

    B. Satisfactory performance exists when_____

_____

_____

    C. Complete performance occurs when_____

_____

_____

    D. Substantial performance occurs when_____

_____

_____

    E. Conditions may be classified as

      1. _____

      2. _____

      3. _____

    F. Tender of performance means_____

_____

_____

15-2   **Discharge by Nonperformance**

    A. When a contract is discharged by agreement _____

_____

      1. Mutual rescission requires _____

_____

_____

      2. Termination by waiver occurs when _____

_____

_____

      3. A novation occurs when_____

_____

_____

      4. Accord and satisfaction means _____

_____

_____

5. A general release is _____

_____

_____

B. When the subject matter of a contract has been destroyed when the contract is entered into _____

_____

_____

C. A discharge by operation of law occurs when _____

_____

_____

D. Breach of contract comes from _____

    1. _____

    2. _____

    3. _____

15-3 Damages and Equitable Remedies

A. Standard damages in contract law include _____

_____

_____

B. Punitive damages are _____

_____

_____

C. Special damages include _____

_____

_____

D. Mitigation of damages requires the injured party to _____

_____

_____

E. Equitable remedies include _____

_____

_____

F. Litigation costs include _____

_____

_____

Legal Concepts

For each statement, write **T** *in the answer column if the statement is true or* **F** *if the statement is false.*

Answer

1. Most contracts are discharged through performance.

  1. _____

2. Ordinarily, substantial performance does not discharge a contract.

  2. _____

3. Satisfactory performance is not a condition of every contract.

  3. _____

4. In a bilateral contract, a condition precedent is a promise that if not performed leads either to rescission or to termination of the entire agreement.

    4. _____

5. Courts usually enforce time stipulations in a contract even when time is not of particular importance.

    5. _____

6. Even though a contract is in writing, an agreed-to rescission is valid if expressed orally.

    6. _____

7. It is not important to make tender even if one knows the other party is not going to perform the contract.

    7. _____

8. Destruction of specific subject matter applicable to an executory contract discharges the contract.

    8. _____

9. Most contractual obligations to pay money do not come to an end when a party files for bankruptcy.

    9. _____

10. When performance of a contract is made illegal by the passage of laws after the formation of the contract, nonperformance is excusable, and the contract may be discharged.

    10. _____

11. Death, disability, or insanity will always discharge the incapacitated party, or the party's estate, from performance of contractual promises.

    11. _____

12. The statute of limitations sets forth specific time periods during which actions may be taken for the collection of debts, claims of damages through torts, and the prosecution of certain crimes.

    12. _____

13. The usual remedy for breach of contract is the payment of money.

    13. _____

14. A court can order specific performance of a contract for the sale of land.

    14. _____

15. Courts allow speculative damages in some cases.

    15. _____

Language of the Law

Select the legal term that best matches each definition.

a. abandonment of contractual obligations
b. anticipatory breach
c. complete performance
d. condition concurrent
e. condition precedent
f. consequential damages
g. discharge
h. general release
i. incidental damages
j. injunction
k. nominal damages
l. satisfactory performance
m. specific performance
n. taxable expenses
o. termination by waiver

Answer

1. Token damages awarded to parties who have experienced an injury to their legal rights but no actual loss

    1. _____

2. A condition that occurs when both parties fully accomplish every term, condition, and promise to which they agree

    2. _____

3. The performance of a contract according to the agreement

    3. _____

4. Stopping performance once it has begun

    4. _____

5. A condition that requires both parties to perform at the same time

    5. _____

6. An award made when a contract is breached to cover expenses incurred by the innocent party in attempting to prevent further loss

6. _____

7. An order of the court requiring a breaching party to do what that party promised to do under the terms of the contract

7. _____

8. An order issued by a court directing that a party do something or refrain from doing something

8. _____

9. Litigation expenses such as the cost of filing the case and issuing subpoenas

9. _____

10. A written and signed document intended to terminate and discharge the contractual obligations of a party

10. _____

Applying the Law

1. Raymond was hired as accompanist for ten concert appearances with Strosky, an operatic tenor. Halfway through the concert tour, Raymond broke two fingers on her right hand, making it impossible to complete her contract. Strosky sued the accompanist for breach of contract, demanding damages for her refusal to continue the tour. Would Strosky be successful in this action? Why or why not?

_____

_____

_____

_____

2. Damico purchased three suits along with other articles of men's wear from Market Mall Men's Shop, using his revolving charge account. Two payments were made over a period of three months after purchase. The balance remained unpaid for a five-year period despite letters, telephone calls, threats of legal action, and Market Mall's giving the account over to a collection agency. Did Damico have a defense against payment of the balance owed if sued by Market Mall Men's Shop? Why or why not?

_____

_____

_____

_____

3. Softknit Industries contracted to sell 100 dozen infant blanket sleepers to Tender Years, a chain store serving young families over a five-state area. Subsequently, the Consumer Product Safety Commission prohibited the manufacture and sale of infant garments from textiles that Softknit had contracted to use in the agreement with Tender Years. Softknit argued that the restrictive regulation could not be applied to contracts made prior to these new rulings. Was Softknit correct? Explain.

_____

_____

_____

_____

4. Prokop signed a contract for purchase of a new car from ABC Sales Company. The seller breached its agreement by not delivering the car. Prokop sought out another car dealer that sold her the same model of car at the same price she had agreed to pay ABC. If Prokop sued the seller for breach of contract and won, what type of damages would be awarded to her?

_____

_____

_____

_____

5. Stevens Machine Company contracted to build and deliver a 150-horsepower steam engine to Valley Generating Company. Delivery of the engine was promised for November 15. On June 25, Stevens notified Valley Generating Company that it was repudiating the contract, giving no justifiable reason for doing so. Valley Generating Company instituted an action for breach of contract immediately. Stevens argued that no action could be brought until after November 15. Was Stevens correct? Why or why not?

_____

_____

_____

_____

6. Marinelli left a computer with Lukens Computer Repair Shop for testing and necessary repairs. Lukens made tests, found what was wrong, but never commenced actual repairs. Nothing was done on the computer for more than three months. After repeated entreaties and calls demanding that the work be done, Marinelli asked for the return of the computer. Lukens refused to give up the set unless Marinelli paid the shop for the time spent on making the tests. Was Lukens correct? Explain.

_____

_____

_____

_____

7. Soul Singers, a country music group, contracted to play for the regular Friday evening dances at Lacey's Lounge. On Monday, Soul Singers' manager called Lacey's Lounge, cancelling their engagement. Lacey petitioned a court of equity, seeking a decree of specific performance that would have required Soul Singers to play their engagement. Would Lacey's Lounge be successful in this petition? Why or why not?

_____

_____

_____

8. Dr. Spires agreed to direct a team doing basic research in toxic chemicals for Chemical Research & Development Corporation. The term of employment was five years, and Spires agreed to accept no employment with other firms doing the same work for two years after expiration of the Chemical Research contract. If Spires does go with another competing firm, could Chemical Research seek relief from a court of equity? Why or why not?

_____

_____

_____

_____

9. Buzby paid a landscape gardener to mow and trim around the Buzby Building. Buzby found that the gardener had missed a few square feet of lawn in the rear of the property. Could Buzby declare the contract breached on grounds of non-performance? Explain.

_____

_____

_____

_____

10. Kirby contracted to have a new house built by Westwood Home Builders. Among other things, Westwood Home Builders agreed that the project would be completed by April 15. Unforeseen difficulties delayed the interior decorating, and the new house was not ready until May 1. Kirby declared the contract breached and refused payment. Was Kirby correct? Why or why not?

_____

_____

_____

_____

Chapter 16   Sale and Lease of Goods

Chapter Outline

16-1   The Sale and Lease of Goods

A.   The law of sales is now part of the _____
_____

B.   Goods are defined as _____
_____

C.   Article 2 of the UCC applies whenever_____
_____
_____

D.   The leasing of goods is governed by Article 2A of the UCC and includes _____
_____
_____

E.   When a contract includes both goods and services_____
_____
_____

16-2   Special Rules for Sales Contracts

The following special rules apply to sales contracts:

A.   _____
B.   _____
C.   _____
D.   _____
E.   _____
F.   _____
G.   _____
H.   _____
I.   _____

16-3   Form of Sales Contracts

A.   A sales contract must be in writing when _____
_____

B.   A lease of goods must be in writing if_____
_____
_____

C. The four exceptions to the general rule are
1. _____
2. _____
3. _____
4. _____

D. The writing that is required to satisfy the UCC must _____
1. indicate that _____
_____
2. mention the _____
_____
3. be signed by _____
_____

E. The federal government has enacted the E-Sign Act, which takes the approach that _____
_____
_____
_____

F. The United Nations Convention on contracts for the International Sale of Goods (CISG) applies to sales between _____
_____
_____

16-4 Auction Sales

In an auction sale,
A. the offer is made by _____
_____
_____

B. the acceptance is made by _____
_____

C. The auctioneer may withdraw the goods at any time before announcing completion of the sale in _____
_____

D. The practice of planting persons in the crowd for the purpose of raising bids is _____
_____

E. In person-to-person Internet auctions, _____
_____
_____

F. Operators of business-to-person Internet auctions, _____
_____
_____

Legal Concepts

For each statement, write **T** *in the answer column if the statement is true or* **F** *if the statement is false.*

                                                             Answer

1. The UCC has been adopted, either in whole or in part, by every state in the United States.   **1.** _____

2. The law of sales does not apply to transactions between private parties.   **2.** _____

3. The unborn young of animals are considered to be goods.   **3.** _____

4. Fish in the sea are considered to be future goods.   **4.** _____

5. When a contract includes both goods and services, the law of sales always applies.   **5.** _____

6. A gift is considered a sale.   **6.** _____

7. A sale occurs every time you buy goods and receive ownership of them.   **7.** _____

8. An enforceable contract for the sale of goods may come about even though some terms are not completely agreed upon.   **8.** _____

9. No consideration is necessary when a merchant promises in writing to hold an offer open for the sale of goods.   **9.** _____

10. A contract to buy "all the oil we need to heat our building" is not allowed under the UCC because the quantity of the goods is not definite.   **10.** _____

11. An agreement modifying a contract for the sale of goods needs no consideration to be binding.   **11.** _____

12. Under the UCC, a contract for the sale of goods for the price of $300 or more must be in writing to be enforceable.   **12.** _____

13. If the seller has made a substantial beginning in manufacturing specially made goods, an oral agreement in any amount is enforceable.   **13.** _____

14. In an auction, without reserve, the auctioneer may withdraw the goods at any time before completion.   **14.** _____

15. In person-to-person auctions, sellers offer items directly to consumers.   **15.** _____

Language of the Law

Select the legal term that best matches each definition.

a. auction with reserve	**f.** future goods	**k.** requirements contract
b. auction without reserve	**g.** goods	**l.** sale
c. bid	**h.** merchant	**m.** Uniform Commercial
d. contract for sale	**i.** open-price terms	Code (UCC)
e. firm offer	**j.** output contract	**n.** usage of trade

1. A present sale or a contract to sell goods at a future time

2. An offer made at an auction

3. Goods that are not yet in existence or under the control of people

4. An agreement to sell all the goods a seller manufactures to a particular buyer

5. An auction where the auctioneer may withdraw the goods at any time before the completion of the sale

6. All things that are movable at the time of identification to the contract for sale

7. A contract in which ownership of goods is transferred from the seller to the buyer for a price

8. An agreement whereby a buyer agrees to buy "all the potatoes we need for our restaurant" from a particular seller

9. The body of law covering sales contracts that has been wholly or partially adopted in every state

10. A merchant's promise to hold an offer open, which must be in writing and requires no consideration

Answer

1. _____
2. _____
3. _____
4. _____
5. _____
6. _____
7. _____
8. _____
9. _____
10. _____

Applying the Law

1. O'Brien agreed to buy a Bluetooth phone from Sykes for $200. The agreement was oral and called for the full amount to be paid in cash the next day. O'Brien later refused to buy the phone. Was the agreement enforce-able? Why or why not?

_____

_____

_____

_____

2. Gregory agreed to buy an unframed oil painting from Callaghan for $489. Later, Gregory asked whether Callaghan would frame the painting at no additional cost. Callaghan agreed. Would Gregory have to provide additional consideration to make Callaghan's added promise enforceable? Explain.

_____

_____

_____

3. Coastal Canning Company contracted to buy 1,600 tons of tuna from Rugby, who operated a tuna fishing fleet. Rugby's ships went to sea and began fishing for the tuna. Two weeks later, when the catch was completed, Rugby's fleet headed for the canning company's pier. Were the tuna in the ship's holds considered future goods at that time? Explain.

_____

_____

_____

_____

4. Modern Electronics agreed to manufacture a 9-room direct TV system that included a digital video recorder for Briggs. The design was so unusual that it was unlikely that anyone else would buy it. The contract price for the completed set was to be $3,500. When the work was finished, Briggs refused to make payment, stating that any sale of goods at that price had to be in writing. Was her argument correct? Why or why not?

_____

_____

_____

_____

5. Dominique selected a new racing bicycle at Best's Cycle Shop. The sales price was $995. The salesperson promised delivery the following afternoon, and Dominique agreed to make payment in full at that time. After the cycle was made ready for delivery, Dominique called the shop and said that the deal was off. Did Best's Cycle Shop have any legal right to damages? Explain.

_____

_____

_____

_____

6. Harrington Manufacturing Company, located in Michigan, ordered 250 tons of soft coal from Allegheny Mining Company, a Pennsylvania firm. The coal was to be delivered and paid for at Harrington's plant located in Ohio. Why would the law that governs this transaction be the same in each of the three states involved?

_____

_____

_____

_____

7. Rose Produce Company contracted with Thornton for 20 tons of green beans to be grown in Thornton's farm and delivered when ready for canning. At the time of their agreement, the seed had not yet been planted. Was this a sale? Why or why not?

_____

_____

_____

_____

8. Crescent Motors, a car dealer, wrote to Webster offering to sell him a Jaguar for $28,000 and agreeing to hold the offer open for one week. Three days later, before Webster accepted, Crescent Motors withdrew its offer. Was the company legally able to do this? Why or why not?

_____

_____

_____

_____

9. Helms was the highest bidder in an auction sale for an antique rolltop desk. The auction was posted to be "with reserve." The auctioneer refused to accept Helms's bid for the desk, saying that it was not high enough, and withdrew the desk from sale. Helms demanded that her bid be accepted. Did the auctioneer have the right to withdraw the desk from the sale? Explain.

_____

_____

_____

_____

10. Codwise was hired by a cartographer to produce street maps for cities and towns by the use of a computer. At the time he was hired, his employer asked him to sign an employment contract, saying that this was required under the Uniform Commercial Code. Was the employer correct? Why or why not?

_____

_____

_____

_____

Chapter 17   Title and Risk of Loss in Sales of Goods

Chapter Outline

17-1   Void and Voidable Title

A. Title is _____
_____
_____

B. Void title is _____
_____
_____

C. Voidable title means _____
_____
_____

D. When goods are entrusted to a merchant who sells them to a third party, the third party receives _____
_____
_____

17-2   The Passage of Title and Risk of Loss

A. Once goods are identified, title passes to the buyer when_____
_____
_____

B. In a shipment contract, both title and risk of loss pass _____
_____
_____

C. In a destination contract, both title and risk of loss pass _____
_____

D. When the contract calls for the buyer to pick up the goods,

   1. title passes to the buyer _____
   _____

   2. risk of loss passes to a _____
   _____

      a. merchant seller, when _____
      _____
      _____

      b. merchant seller, when _____
      _____
      _____

E. Title to fungible goods may pass _____

_____

_____

F. When a document of title is used, both title and risk of loss pass_____

_____

_____

G. The parties may enter into an agreement setting forth _____

_____

_____

H. Title to goods revests in the seller when _____

_____

_____

I. The international law does not address questions dealing with _____

_____

_____

J. The rules governing the passage of risk of loss are addressed _____

_____

_____

17-3   **Sales with Right of Return**   **A.** When goods are sold on approval, they remain the property of the seller until _____

_____

                                         B. On a sale or return, title belongs to _____

_____

_____

17-4   **Insurable Interest**   Buyers may insure goods the moment a_____

_____

_____

Legal Concepts

For each statement, write **T** *in the answer column if the statement is true or* **F** *if the statement is false.*   **Answer**

1. Buyers of goods acquire whatever title their sellers have to the property.   **1.** _____

2. Anyone with voidable title to goods is able to transfer good title to others.   **2.** _____

3. The owner of goods who entrusts them to a merchant retains title to the goods if the merchant sells them to someone else in the ordinary course of business.   **3.** _____

4. Before title can pass from the seller to the buyer, goods must be identified to the contract.   4. _____

5. In a shipment contract, risk of loss passes from the seller to the buyer when the goods are delivered to a carrier.   5. _____

6. When terms of shipment do not specify shipping point or destination, it is assumed to be f.o.b. (free on board) the place of destination.   6. _____

7. If the seller is a merchant, the risk of loss passes when the buyer tenders delivery if the contract calls for the buyer to pick up the goods.   7. _____

8. Title to fungible goods may pass without the necessity of separating goods sold from the bulk.   8. _____

9. When a document of title is used in a sales transaction, both title and risk of loss pass to the buyer when the document is delivered to the buyer.   9. _____

10. Parties may enter into an agreement setting forth the exact time that risk of loss passes from the seller to the buyer.   10. _____

11. When the seller sends goods to the buyer that do not meet the contract requirements and are therefore unacceptable, the risk of loss remains with the seller.   11. _____

12. Goods held by the buyer on approval are subject to the claims of the buyer's creditors.   12. _____

13. Goods held on sale or return must be returned at the seller's risk and expense.   13. _____

14. A person must have an insurable interest in certain property in order to place insurance on it.   14. _____

15. Both the buyer and the seller may have an insurable interest in goods that are identified to the contract.   15. _____

Language of the Law

Select the legal term that best matches each definition.

a. c.f.
b. c.i.f.
c. c.o.d.
d. destination contract
e. document of title
f. f.a.s. vessel
g. f.o.b.
h. f.o.b. the place of destination
i. f.o.b. the place of shipment
j. fungible goods
k. sale on approval
l. sale or return
m. shipment contract
n. voidable title
o. void titles

Answer

1. Contracts under which title is transferred when the seller tenders the goods at the place of destination   1. _____

2. Goods of which any unit is the equivalent of any like unit   2. _____

3. A term that means "cash on delivery"   3. _____

4. A term meaning "free alongside"   4. _____

5. No title at all   5. _____

6. A paper that proves that the person who possesses it is entitled to receive goods named in the document

7. Title that may be voided by a minor or injured party if he or she elects to do so

8. A term meaning "free on board"

9. A sale that allows goods to be returned even though they conform to the contract and the goods are delivered primarily for resale

10. A term that indicates that goods will be transported free of charge to the place from which the goods are to be shipped

6. _____

7. _____

8. _____

9. _____

10. _____

Applying the Law

1. Des Moines Grain Co. sold 150,000 bushels of corn to Eastern Milling Co., giving Eastern a grain elevator receipt from Elevator No. 281. While still in the elevator, the corn was destroyed by fire. Eastern argued that Des Moines must assume the loss. Was Eastern correct? Why or why not?

_____

_____

_____

_____

2. Electronic Sales Co. sold Feldman, a consumer, a flat-screen TV for $2,000, promising that if she did not like the unit after one week she could return it and get her money back. If the unit suffered damage during that week, would the seller have to return Feldman's money? Why or why not?

_____

_____

_____

_____

3. Goods were shipped to Mann Company, terms f.o.b., c.o.d. Mann owed $350 on the shipment, plus shipping charges. When notified of the arrival of the goods, Mann demanded their delivery without payment of the amount due, stating that title to the goods passed to the company when shipped. Did Mann have the right to the goods? Why or why not?

_____

_____

_____

_____

4. Jefferson bought a piano from Hamlin Piano Company with a condition that it would be delivered. Hamlin loaded the piano into its truck, but the piano was damaged when the driver hit an abutment. Jefferson had selected the piano, paid for it, and had it tuned before it was taken from the shop. Did Hamlin or Jefferson suffer the risk of loss to the piano? Explain.

_____

_____

_____

_____

5. Winter Sewing Machine Company agreed to deliver a sewing machine to Hopkins for a two-week trial. If Hopkins did not want to buy the machine, he agreed to notify the seller to come pick it up. The two weeks passed and Hopkins did not call the seller. After a month, he received a bill for $375, the price that Winter had stated to Hopkins. He refused to honor the bill, claiming that approval of the sale had never been given. Could Winter collect the $375? Why or why not?

_____

_____

_____

_____

6. Knapp, through fraudulent means, persuaded Rigby to sell her an antique Chippendale mirror that had been in Rigby's family for generations. Knapp told Rigby that the mirror was of little value. Knapp then sold it to a museum for $2,500. Rigby demanded the return of the mirror from the museum, claiming that Knapp's title was voidable and the museum could not continue as the owner. Did Rigby win the case? Why or why not?

_____

_____

_____

_____

7. Hume, who was not a merchant, agreed to sell his tractor to Warne for $1,500. Hume told Warne that it was available for him to pick up at any time. Warne paid for the tractor and said that he would pick it up the next day. A week later the tractor was stolen from Hume's property. It had not been picked up by Warne as agreed. Must Warne or Hume suffer the loss? Why?

_____
_____
_____
_____

8. Lee bought and paid for a new watch from a jewelry store. The seller agreed to keep the watch until it was convenient for Lee to pick it up. Another clerk, uninformed of the transaction, sold the same watch to Hill. Would Lee be able to claim the watch from Hill? Explain.

_____
_____
_____
_____

9. Esposito bought a guaranteed used car from Sanders Used-Car Sales. After he had driven the car for several months, the police charged him with driving a stolen vehicle. The car was confiscated and returned to the real owner, from whom it had been stolen six months earlier. Did Esposito have rights to the car? Why or why not?

_____
_____
_____
_____

10. Ward ordered heavy machinery from a company in Moline, Illinois. The machinery was shipped to Ward, terms f.o.b. Moline. En route to its destination in Los Angeles, the machinery was destroyed when the freight train derailed and caught fire. Ward refused to honor the bill for the machinery. Would he be required to pay for it? Explain.

_____
_____
_____
_____

Chapter 18   Performance and Breach of the Sales Contract

Chapter Outline

18-1   **Obligations of the Parties**

    A. The seller is obligated to _____

    _____

    B. The buyer is obligated to _____

    _____

    C. All parties must act _____

    _____

18-2   **Tender of Performance**

    A. Tender is necessary in order to _____

    _____

    B. The seller's obligation to deliver the goods is on the condition that the buyer _____

    _____

    C. Under international law, the buyer must pay the price for the goods and take delivery of them as _____

    _____

    _____

18-3   **Buyer's Rights and Duties Upon Delivery of Improper Goods**

    A. Except when goods are shipped c.o.d. or when the contract provides for payment against a document of title, the buyer has the right to inspect the goods_____

    _____

    B. When defective goods or goods not of the kind specified in the contract are delivered, the buyer may elect to

        1. _____

        _____

        2. _____

        _____

        3. _____

        _____

    C. Merchant buyers have a duty after the rejection of goods to _____

    _____

    _____

D. Acceptance of goods takes place when the buyer does any of the following:

1. _____

2. _____

3. _____

4. _____

E. A buyer may revoke an acceptance if _____

_____

F. Under international law, if the goods do not conform, the buyer must

_____

_____

_____

18-4 Seller's Right to Cure Improper Tender

A. To cure an improper tender means to _____

_____

_____

B. Under international law, the seller may cure any defect in the goods if the goods were delivered before the date of delivery only _____

_____

_____

18-5 Breach of Contract

A. Under the UCC, when either party repudiates the contract before the time for performance, the injured party may _____

_____

_____

B. When a buyer breaches a sales contract, the seller may

1. _____

_____

2. _____

_____

3. _____

_____

4. _____

_____

5. _____

_____

6. _____

_____

C. When a seller breaches a sales contract, the buyer may

1. _____
_____

2. _____
_____

3 _____
_____

4. _____
_____

5. _____
_____

6. _____
_____

D. In general, an action for breach of contract for sale must be brought

_____

_____

_____

E. Under international law, damages for breach of contract by one party consist of a sum _____

_____

Legal Concepts

For each statement, write **T** *in the answer column if the statement is true or* **F** *if the statement is false.*

Answer

1. In a sales contract, both the buyer and the seller are obligated to act in good faith.

1. _____

2. The court must enforce a contract that it finds to be unconscionable.

2. _____

3. The court often looks at the usage of trade to supplement the express terms of a contract.

3. _____

4. The buyer is not obligated to pay for goods if the seller has not made tender of delivery.

4. _____

5. Tender of delivery must be made at a reasonable hour of the day.

5. _____

6. The seller has no right to demand payment in legal tender.

6. _____

7. Legally, a contract for the sale of goods may never require payment before inspection of the goods delivered.

7. _____

8. When defective goods are delivered, the buyer may accept any commercial unit and reject the rest.

8. _____

9. A merchant must make a reasonable effort to sell rejected perishable goods.

9. _____

10. A revocation of acceptance is not effective until the buyer notifies the seller of it.

    10. _____

11. The seller always has the right to cure nonconforming goods.

    11. _____

12. When either party to a sales contract repudiates the contract before the time for performance, the injured party must wait until the actual time for performance before bringing suit.

    12. _____

13. Both incidental and consequential damages may not be awarded in the same case.

    13. _____

14. When improper goods are delivered, the buyer may keep them and ask the seller for an adjustment.

    14. _____

15. Lawsuits have a time limit within which suit must be brought.

    15. _____

Language of the Law

Select the legal term that best matches each definition.

a. anticipatory breach
b. carrier
c. commercial unit
d. cover
e. cure

f. insolvent
g. legal tender
h. liquidated damages
i. specific performance
j. stoppage in transit

k. tender of delivery
l. tender of payment
m. tender of performance
n. unconscionable contract
o. writ of replevin

    Answer

1. The remedy of buying similar goods from someone else and suing the seller for the difference between the agreed price and the cost of the purchase

    1. _____

2. That which occurs when the parties to a contract for sale offer to do that which they have agreed to do

    2. _____

3. A contract that is oppressively one-sided, giving unfair advantage to one of the parties

    3. _____

4. The act by the seller of offering to turn the goods over to the buyer

    4. _____

5. A single whole for the purpose of a sale

    5. _____

6. The exact amount due in U.S. currency

    6. _____

7. A decree granted by a court of equity that requires the seller to deliver unique or rare goods described in the sales agreement to the buyer

    7. _____

8. The act of the buyer of offering to turn the money over to the seller

    8. _____

9. A court action used to require the seller to convey identified goods to the purchaser who has been unable to obtain the goods elsewhere

    9. _____

10. The right of a seller to have the delivery of goods stopped before they reach their destination

    10. _____

Name_____   Date_____

Applying the Law

1. DiVito Baking Co. ordered 1,000 bushels of Baldwin apples from Groveland Orchards for use in making apple pies. By mistake, Groveland Orchards shipped MacIntosh apples, which DiVito could not use. Could DiVito allow the MacIntosh apples to rot while it waited for Groveland to correct the error? Explain.

_____

_____

_____

2. Eye Care Outlet entered into a contract to buy 1,000 eyeglass frames from Weeks. The frames were to be delivered on October 15. On June 15, four months before the delivery date, Eye Care notified Weeks that it was canceling the order. Could Weeks bring suit immediately against Eye Care Outlet for breach of contract? Why or why not?

_____

_____

_____

3. Style Rite Furniture Company ordered eight complete bedroom sets from National Furniture Supply Company. When one of the beds was found to be broken, Style Rite rejected not only the broken bed but also the rest of the pieces in that particular set of furniture. Was Style Rite's rejection legal? Why or why not?

_____

_____

4. Rousette signed an agreement to buy an antique mirror of unusual design from Amirault, who agreed in writing to deliver it in one week. Two days later, the seller telephoned Rousette, saying that she had decided to keep the mirror for her own personal use because of its rarity. She assured Rousette that she would return his deposit in full. Could Rousette bring an action against Amirault to receive the mirror? Explain.

_____

_____

5. Tiny Tots Toy Company entered into a contract with Superior Electric Train Company for the purchase of 100 electric train sets. By mistake, the train sets were delivered to Tiny Tim's Toy Company. Nevertheless, when billed for the trains, Tiny Tots paid for them, not realizing the error. Five years later, when its books were audited in preparation for a computerized accounting system, Tiny Tots discovered that it had not received the electric train sets. Could Tiny Tots recover damages from Superior Electric Train Company for failing to deliver the goods? Why or why not?

_____

_____

6. Davis, who had lost her job and was on welfare, was approached by a fast-talking salesperson one afternoon as she was sweeping off her front sidewalk. After discussing her difficulties of being out of a job and relying on welfare to support her five children, the salesperson talked her into signing a contract to install aluminum siding on her small bungalow for $20,000. Later that day, Davis learned that such a job was worth no more than $2,000. On what grounds might Davis be able to have the contract declared void?

_____

_____

_____

7. Sanborn ordered a leather jacket from the Amesbury Leather Company, which agreed to ship the jacket to Sanborn c.o.d. When the jacket was delivered, Sanborn insisted that she be allowed to inspect it before paying for it. Did she have the right to do so? Explain.

_____

_____

_____

8. Vaughn Corporation sent one of its employees to pick up some parts it had ordered from Valley Supply Company. The employee offered to pay for the parts with a Vaughn Corporation check made payable to Valley Supply for the correct amount. Valley Supply refused to take the check, saying that it had to have cash before it could release the goods. Was Valley Supply within its rights? Why or why not?

_____

_____

_____

9. Meehan agreed to sell 500 cases of canned vegetables to Katz for $3,500, f.o.b. Katz's warehouse. Meehan refused to deliver the goods, however, until he received payment, and Katz would not pay for the goods until they were delivered. Meehan sued Katz for breach of contract. Would Meehan win the case? Why or why not?

_____

_____

_____

10. Lenz agreed to buy McIsaac's secondhand Ferrari automobile, although it did not run, upon being assured by McIsaac that the parts to make it run had been ordered and would arrive within a month. McIsaac promised to put the car in running order when the parts arrived. Lenz paid for the car and had it towed to her property. Three months later, the parts still had not arrived, and the car sat idle, unable to be used. Could Lenz legally return the car to McIsaac? Give a reason for your answer.

_____

_____

_____

Chapter 19   Warranties and Product Liability

Chapter Outline

19-1   Warranty Protection

A. An express warranty is _____
_____
_____

B. Express warranties arise in the following ways:

    1. _____

    2. _____

    3. _____

C. The following rules must be followed when advertising goods for sale in interstate commerce:

    1. _____

    2. _____

    3. _____

D. Under international law (CISG), sellers must deliver goods that
_____
_____

E. Under the Magnuson-Moss Warranty Act, when a written warranty is given to a consumer, all of the following must be done:

    1. _____

    2. _____

    3. _____

F. An implied warranty is _____
_____
_____

G. To be merchantable, goods must at least

    1. _____

    2. _____

    3. _____

    4. _____

    5. _____

    6. _____

H. The warranty of fitness for a particular purpose arises when _____
_____
_____

I. Other implied warranties may arise from _____

_____

J. Whenever goods are sold, the seller warrants that the title _____

_____

K. To recover damages for a breach of warranty, buyers of defective goods must notify _____

_____

19-2   Exclusion of Warranties

A. To exclude the implied warranty of merchantability _____

_____

B. To exclude the implied warranty of fitness for a particular purpose

_____

C. Implied warranties may also be excluded by _____

_____

D. Many states protect consumers by saying that _____

_____

E. By statute in some states, the handling of human blood is _____

_____

_____

19-3   Privity Not Required

Under the Uniform Commercial Code (UCC), warranties extend to people who _____

_____

19-4   Product Liability

A. Negligence may be defined as _____

_____

_____

B. Under the doctrine of strict liability, it is not necessary to prove

_____

_____

_____

Legal Concepts

For each statement, write **T** *in the answer column if the statement is true*   **Answer**
or **F** *if the statement is false.*

1. Express warranties may be made by both merchant and
   nonmerchant sellers.   1. _____
2. An express warranty can be created without the use of formal
   words such as *guarantee*.   2. _____
3. Whenever a seller of goods makes a statement of fact about the
   goods to a buyer as part of a transaction, an implied warranty
   is created.   3. _____
4. Any description of the goods that is made part of the basis of
   the bargain creates an express warranty.   4. _____
5. The Magnuson-Moss Warranty Act applies only when written
   warranties are made voluntarily on consumer products.   5. _____
6. An implied warranty is created when a sample is made part of
   the basis of the bargain.   6. _____
7. A full warranty is only conferred upon the original buyer of a
   product.   7. _____
8. To be merchantable, fungible goods must be of fair, average
   quality.   8. _____
9. A claim for breach of warranty of merchantability can be made
   only if a defect exists when the goods are purchased.   9. _____
10. An innocent purchaser of stolen goods may retain title to the
    goods.   10. _____
11. Implied warranties may be excluded by having buyers examine
    the goods or the sample.   11. _____
12. In some states, including Florida and Massachusetts, the
    procurement, processing, storage, and distribution of human
    blood is called a sale rather than a service.   12. _____
13. Failure of the buyer to notify the seller about defective goods
    within a reasonable time will prevent the buyer from receiving
    breach-of-warranty money damages.   13. _____
14. Injured parties are often more successful in bringing suit for
    breach of warranty of merchantability than in bringing suit for
    negligence.   14. _____
15. For recovery under the doctrine of strict liability, the party
    bringing the suit must prove negligence on the part of the
    manufacturer or seller when injury results from a defective
    product.   15. _____

Language of the Law

Select the legal term that best matches each definition.

a. consequential damages
b. consumer products
c. express warranty
d. full warranty
e. implied warranty
f. limited warranty
g. negligence
h. product liability
i. punitive damages
j. strict liability
k. usage of trade
l. warranty of fitness for a particular purpose
m. warranty of merchantability
n. warranty of title

Answer

1. A written guarantee that does not meet all the requirements of a full warranty

    1. _____

2. A written guarantee under which a defective product will be repaired without charge within a reasonable time after a complaint has been made about it

    2. _____

3. Law under which an injured buyer may recover damages from either the manufacturer, seller, or supplier because of a product's unsafe condition

    3. _____

4. The failure to exercise that degree of care that a reasonably prudent person would have exercised under the same circumstances

    4. _____

5. An assurance by the seller of goods that the title is good and the transfer rightful

    5. _____

6. A warranty created by an affirmation of fact, a description of the goods, or by a sample or model

    6. _____

7. Damages that do not flow directly and immediately from an act

    7. _____

8. Under this theory of law, manufacturers have the duty to design reasonably safe products

    8. _____

9. A warranty that is given only when the seller is a merchant

    9. _____

10. A warranty that comes about when the buyer relies on the seller's skill and judgment to select the goods

    10. _____

Applying the Law

1. As Kimball drove away from the dealership where she had just purchased a new car, the steering mechanism in the new car failed. The car swerved out of control, injuring three pedestrians. Would the injured pedestrians have a legal claim against the car manufacturer? Why or why not?

_____

_____

_____

2. Muto ordered a set of illustrated history books from Sterline Publishing Company. Samples shown by the publisher's representative were on the best grade of paper and were printed in brilliant colors. When the books arrived, Muto was disappointed by the weak coloring and the cheap paper used in production. For what reason did he have a right of action in this situation?

_____

_____

_____

3. Enos sold a painting to Ojeda, saying that it was an original by a well-known nineteenth-century artist. Ojeda found out afterward that the painting was a copy of the original. The seller refused to negotiate an adjustment. Did Ojeda have a remedy against Enos for breach of warranty? Why or why not?

_____

_____

_____

_____

4. Gonzale selected and bought a television dish from Drew's TV and Supply Shop without seeking advice from the shop owner. The reception through the new dish was very poor. Another model would have given perfect reception. Did the shop breach the implied warranty of fitness for a particular purpose? Explain.

_____

_____

_____

_____

5. Zukas bought a new electric snowblower. A week later, Zukas's son was injured while using the snowblower. The injury was caused by a defect in the product. The manufacturer maintained that its liability was to Zukas only, not to Zukas's son. Was the manufacturer's argument correct? Why or why not?

_____

_____

_____

_____

6. Manzi read the description of a sport coat in a brochure he received from a mail-order house. He ordered the sport coat, enclosing a check with the order. When the sport coat arrived, Manzi found that it was different from the one described in the brochure. Did the mail-order house breach a warranty in this transaction? Explain.

_____

_____

_____

_____

7. Codwise discovered that the time-set mechanism on her automatic coffee maker did not work the day she bought it from her local appliance store. Ten months later, Codwise notified the appliance store of the defect, and the store refused to remedy the situation. Did Codwise have a cause of action against the store? Why or why not?

_____

_____

_____

_____

8. Kelley needed a power lawn mower. The seller, a merchant, guaranteed that his machine was sharp and would do a good job on Kelley's lawn. Kelley was invited to try the machine out around the seller's shop. The motor ran perfectly, although there was no grass on which he could test its real efficiency. He bought the mower, but returned it the following day. According to Kelley, it would not cut the grass. The seller defended the sale by reminding Kelley of his examination of the machine. Could Kelley recover the money paid for the ineffective mower? Explain.

_____

_____

_____

9. Bach worked as a machinist supervisor. Work done in the shop allowed only 0.0001 of an inch tolerance in machine drive shafts for aircraft engines. He bought a micrometer, telling the company the specifications needed in this work. A defect in the measuring instrument resulted in the loss of $200,000 in time and materials in the precision work supervised by Bach. Could Bach's company recover this loss through an action against the seller? Why or why not?

_____

_____

_____

_____

10. Randall received a tainted blood transfusion in a hospital located in Massachusetts. Does she have recourse under the implied warranty of merchantability? Explain.

_____

_____

_____

_____

Chapter 20   Consumer Protection

Chapter Outline

20-1   Federal and State Consumer Protection Laws

    A. Consumer protection laws apply to transactions between_____
_____
_____

    B. The FTC Act states that_____
_____
_____

    C. The FTC Act applies to businesses that sell real estate, goods, or services in _____
_____

20-2   Unfair or Deceptive Acts or Practices

    A. It is unfair or deceptive for a seller to make fraudulent misrepresentations, that is,_____
_____

    B. While some work-at-home plans are legitimate,_____
_____
_____

    C. People who receive unordered merchandise through the mail may
_____
_____

    D. The purpose of bait and switch advertising is to _____
_____
_____

    E. The federal Odometer Law prohibits people from _____
_____
_____

20-3   The FTC Trade Regulation Rules

    A. The Used Car Rule requires used car dealers to _____
_____
_____

    B. Under the cooling-off rule, sales of consumer goods or services over
_____
_____

    C. The negative option rule applies when _____
_____
_____

D. Identity theft occurs when someone _____

_____

_____

E. Reporting problems with online transactions involving foreign countries allows government agencies to _____

_____

_____

F. Under the Can Spam Act, unsolicited email messages must_____

_____

_____

G. Slamming is the _____

_____

H. Under the Mail, Telephone, Internet, or Fax Rule, sellers must _____

_____

_____

I. The FTC's Do Not Call Registry makes it easier _____

_____

_____

J. FTC regulations require that people who dial 900 numbers be warned of_____

_____

20-4 **Consumer Product Safety Act**

The Consumer Product Safety Act was passed to protect consumers from

_____

_____

_____

_____

20-5 **Consumer Leasing Act**

The Consumer Leasing Act requires leasing companies to _____

_____

_____

_____

_____

20-6 **Consumer Credit Laws**

A. Under the Truth-in-Lending Act, lenders must disclose to borrowers

1. _____

2. _____

B. Under the Equal Credit Opportunity Act, people who apply for credit may not be asked _____

_____

    C.   Under the Truth-in-Lending Act, credit cardholders are not
responsible for_____

       _____

    D.   Under the Fair Credit Reporting Act, consumers have the right to
know _____

       _____

    E.   The Fair Credit Billing Act establishes a procedure for _____

       _____

       _____

    F.   The Fair Debt Collection Practices Act was passed to prevent_____

       _____

       _____

Legal Concepts

*For each statement, write **T** in the answer column if the statement is true
or **F** if the statement is false.*

                                                                 Answer

1. Under the Negative Option Rule, sellers must tell subscribers
how many selections they must buy.   **1.** _____

2. If you have been slammed and have not paid the bill, you must
pay before 30 days are up.   **2.** _____

3. The FTC Act applies to all intrastate commerce.   **3.** _____

4. Under the Used Car Rule, the Buyer's Guide must post a statement
listing the specific systems that are covered by the warranty.   **4.** _____

5. Under the Cooling-off Rule, sales of consumer goods or
services made at a customer's home may be cancelled within
three business days if the price of the sale is more than $25.   **5.** _____

6. Consumers who order goods by mail must receive either their
goods or an option notice within sixty days.   **6.** _____

7. Failure to disclose to a buyer any fact that would cause the
buyer not to enter into the contract is a deceptive or unfair act. **7.** _____

8. People who receive unordered merchandise through the mail
must return it to the sender.   **8.** _____

9. It is illegal to disconnect or reset the odometer of a motor vehicle. **9.** _____

10. The Consumer Product Safety Act only protects consumers
from hazardous products that are Americanmade.   **10.** _____

11. The Consumer Leasing Act applies to daily rentals of personal
property for personal, family, or household use.   **11.** _____

12. Under the Truth-in-Lending Act, lenders must disclose both
the finance charge and the annual percentage rate.   **12.** _____

13. People who apply for credit may legally be asked whether they
are divorced or widowed.   **13.** _____

14. Under the Truth-in-Lending Act, credit cardholders are responsible for the first $100 only of any unauthorized charges.

14. _____

15. Once your number is registered in the National Do Not Call Registry, it will remain there for three years.

15. _____

Language of the Law

Select the legal term that best matches each definition.

a. annual percentage rate
b. bait-and-switch scheme
c. balloon payment
d. Buyer's Guide
e. Can Spam Act
f. commerce
g. consent order
h. consumer
i. Cooling-off Rule
j. finance charge
k. interstate commerce
l. intrastate commerce
m. 900 telephone number
n. Telemarketing Sales Rule
o. Used Car Rule

Answer

1. Insincere offers to sell a product that the advertiser does not intend to sell

1. _____

2. The actual cost of a loan in dollars and cents

2. _____

3. The consumer pays by the minute for using this service

3. _____

4. A way in which the FTC may cause a company to stop a disputed practice without making the company admit to any guilt

4. _____

5. A person who buys or rents things from a business for personal use

5. _____

6. Business activity that involves more than one state

6. _____

7. An informative sticker placed in the window of a used car offered for sale

7. _____

8. Under this rule, calling times are restricted to the hours between 8 a.m. and 9 p.m.

8. _____

9. Local business activity carried on within state boundaries

9. _____

10. Under this rule, consumers are given an opportunity to change their minds after signing contracts with people who come to their houses

10. _____

Applying the Law

1. Duffy ordered some printed stationery from a mail-order firm, enclosing a check in payment. After waiting forty-five days and receiving no response, Duffy canceled the order and demanded the return of her money. Was Duffy within her rights? Explain.

_____

_____

_____

2. Tin Kee Ng, a single parent of three children, applied for credit at a local department store. The store manager refused the credit application because Ng was receiving welfare payments. Could Ng challenge the store's refusal to extend credit? Why or why not?

_____

_____

_____

3. Guzman, who lived in New Jersey, bought a stereo cabinet from a dealer while visiting friends in North Carolina. She paid for the cabinet with a credit card, and the dealer agreed to ship it to her home in New Jersey. The cabinet that arrived in New Jersey displayed defective workmanship, and the credit card issuer refused to adjust Guzman's bill. Was Guzman entitled to relief under the Fair Credit Billing Act? Explain.

_____

_____

_____

_____

4. Jareo went to an appliance store to buy a microwave oven that was advertised in the newspaper. The salesperson discouraged her from buying the advertised microwave, saying that it was small, of poor quality, and did not have a turntable. The salesperson tried to talk Jareo into buying a more expensive microwave of better quality. Did the salesperson violate the law? Explain.

_____

_____

_____

_____

5. Blair sold his three-year-old car to Wilson. Two years earlier, when the car's odometer had malfunctioned after running 7,000 miles, Blair had installed a new odometer, which was set at zero miles. On the bill of sale to Wilson, Blair disclosed the present mileage reading. Did Blair violate the law? Explain.

_____

_____

_____

6. Carlucci applied for and received a credit card from an oil company. Shortly after the card was received, it was stolen and used for the unauthorized purchase of gasoline, tires, and a battery, totaling $574.49. Carlucci refused to pay for the merchandise purchased with the stolen card. Was Carlucci responsible for all of the unauthorized purchases that were made on the stolen card? Why or why not?

_____

_____

_____

_____

7. Romano signed a contract for the purchase of a $4,000 above-ground pool and accessories sold to him by a sales representative who visited all the homes in the neighborhood. Romano made a $300 down payment and agreed to pay the balance in monthly installments of $112. After the sales representative departed, Romano realized that the monthly payments were more than he could safely afford. The following morning Romano wrote to the supplier stating that he wished to cancel the agreement. Could this contract be canceled? Why or why not?

_____

_____

_____

_____

8. Ley had been turned down for credit by several commercial establishments before discovering that the refusals were prompted by a bad credit report furnished by a credit bureau. How can Ley learn what is in his credit bureau file?

_____

_____

_____

_____

9. A credit card was mailed to Jacoby, although she had not applied for it. The card was stolen from her mailbox and unauthorized purchases amounting to $260 were made. Would Jacoby be liable for any of the purchases made on the unsolicited credit card? Why or why not?

_____

_____

_____

_____

10. Defano received several telephone calls at about 9:30 p.m. from a telemarketer from a neighboring state trying to sell her new windows. How can she best stop receiving unwanted calls?

_____

_____

_____

_____

Chapter 21   Personal Property

Chapter Outline

21-1   Personal Property

A. Broadly speaking, personal property is _____
_____
_____

B. Intangible personal property is _____
_____
_____

C. When personal property is owned solely by one person, it is said to be owned _____
_____
_____

D. When two or more people own personal property as tenants in common, each _____
_____

E. When two or more people own personal property as joint tenants, each _____
_____

F. The finder of lost property has a legal responsibility to _____
_____
_____

G. If lost property is found on the counter of a store, it is considered __
_____
_____

H. Abandoned property is _____
_____
_____

I. If an abandoned shipwreck is found outside the boundaries of a state, either _____
_____
_____

J. The three requirements for a transfer to be considered a gift are
   1. _____
   2. _____
   3. _____

K. Under the Uniform Transfers to Minors Act (UTMA), minors are assured_____
_____

L. A gift in *causa mortis* is _____

_____

_____

M. The Uniform Anatomical Gift Act concerns gifts of _____

_____

_____

N. A thief acquires _____

_____

_____

21-2 Intellectual Property

A. A patent gives the owner exclusive right to _____

_____

_____

B. A utility patent is granted to someone who _____

_____

C. A design patent is granted to someone who _____

_____

D. A plant patent is granted to someone who _____

_____

E. To be legally protected, a patented item must _____

_____

F. Under the Paris Convention for the Protection of Industrial Property, each country guarantees _____

_____

G. A copyright is a right granted to _____

_____

H. The copyright law protects original works for _____

_____

I. Copyrighted material may be reproduced without permission if

_____

J. The Computer Software Copyright Act includes _____

_____

_____

K. The function of a trademark is to_____

_____

_____

L. Trademarks can be established in three different ways

1. _____

2. _____

3. _____

M. A federal trademark registration remains in force_____

_____

_____

N. Companies can lose their trademark protection if_____

_____

_____

O. Businesses often protect trade secrets by having employees_____

_____

_____

Legal Concepts

For each statement, write **T** *in the answer column if the statement is true or* **F** *if the statement is false.*

Answer

1. All personal property has substance that can be touched.

    1. _____

2. Money due on a note or contract is not personal property.

    2. _____

3. The finder of lost property has a legal responsibility to make an effort to learn the identity of the owner and return the property to that person.

    3. _____

4. Under the UTMA, the custodianship terminates when a minor reaches the age of eighteen.

    4. _____

5. Under the Kiddie Tax, all income of a minor under the age of fourteen is taxable to the minor rather than to the minor's parents.

    5. _____

6. A thief acquires title to goods that are stolen and therefore can convey a good title to someone else.

    6. _____

7. A patent may be obtained if the subject matter of the patent would be obvious to a person having ordinary skill in the field.

    7. _____

8. Under the common law, trademarks may be established by usage rather than by registration with the state or federal government.

    8. _____

9. In some states, gift certificate money that is unclaimed after a certain number of years must be transferred to the state under the abandoned property law.

    9. _____

10. If an abandoned shipwreck is found in the submerged land of any state of the United States, the *law of salvage* applies.

    10. _____

11. A domain name for a web site may not be copyrighted.

    11. _____

12. To be legally protected, a patented item must be marked with the word *patent* followed by the patent number.

12. _____

13. Copyrights give to their owner the exclusive legal right to reproduce, publish, and sell their original work for the life of the author.

13. _____

14. Under the fair-use doctrine, copyrighted materials for noncommercial purposes may be reproduced without permission if the use of the materials is reasonable and not harmful to the rights of the copyright owner.

14. _____

15. It is no longer necessary to put © or the word *copyright* followed by the date and the name of the owner on a copyrighted work.

15. _____

Language of the Law

Select the legal term that best matches each definition.

a. copyright
b. design patent
c. donee
d. donor
e. fair use doctrine

f. gift in *causa mortis*
g. gift *inter vivos*
h. joint tenants
i. personal property
j. public domain

k. salvage
l. severalty
m. tenants in common
n. trademark
o. utility panel

Answer

1. Any word, name, symbol, or device adopted and used by a manufacturer to identify goods and distinguish them from those sold by others

1. _____

2. The person who gives a gift

2. _____

3. A gift given by someone in anticipation of his or her own death from a known cause

3. _____

4. Legal rights that protect the writings of authors and the works of artists from unauthorized reproduction

4. _____

5. Everything that can be owned other than real estate

5. _____

6. A patent granted for 14 years that protects the way an article looks

6. _____

7. The reward given to persons who voluntarily assist a sinking ship to recover its cargo from peril or loss

7. _____

8. Owners of property, with each owner's share of the property passing to his or her heirs upon death

8. _____

9. Anything owned by the public and not given copyright

9. _____

10. The state of sole ownership of a single property

10. _____

Applying the Law

1. Gage, fearing death from severe injuries suffered in an automobile accident, gave his friend a valuable diamond and ruby ring. Gage recovered from his injuries. Must the friend give the ring back if Gage wants it back? Why or why not?

_____

_____

_____

2. Stephanie Gregory, who was six years old, received a gift of money from her grandfather, who followed the procedures established by the UTMA. The current year's interest and dividends earned from the investment amounted to $820. Was the income taxed at her parents' top tax rate? Explain.

_____

_____

_____

_____

3. Sanchez used a distinctive trademark on boxes of candy he made and sold locally. A competitor, Russo, copied and used the trademark on boxes of popcorn that she sold locally. Sanchez claimed that he was protected by the federal trademark laws. Was he correct? Why or why not?

_____

_____

_____

_____

4. Tubbs found a gold watch in an airport waiting room. There was nothing to identify the watch. Tubbs put it in his pocket, satisfied that "finders keepers, losers weepers" was the law. Was Tubbs correct? Explain.

_____

_____

_____

_____

5. Kimball left her pocketbook on a chair beside the table in the restaurant where she had dinner. St. Pierre, the next customer of the restaurant who sat at that table, discovered the pocketbook and told the manager about it. The manager allowed St. Pierre to keep the pocketbook. Kimball contends that the manager violated the law. Was Kimball correct? Why or why not?

_____

_____

_____

_____

6. Cruz bought some tools from LaRue without knowledge that LaRue had stolen them from a construction site. Later, when the true owner was discovered, Cruz argued that he should be able to keep the tools because he had no knowledge that the tools were stolen. Is Cruz's argument sound? Why or why not?

_____

_____

_____

_____

7. Snyder obtained a patent on a unique tool that he invented. Soon after the tool was manufactured by Snyder and placed on the market, Ram Tool Company copied it without permission and began selling it. When sued for patent infringement, Ram Tool Company pointed out that the word "patent" and its number were not placed upon the tool by the original manufacturer. Will Snyder win the patent infringement suit? Explain.

_____

_____

_____

_____

8. Posada, who worked in the evenings, videotaped a favorite TV program each evening to view when she got home from work. The program was copyrighted. Was the copyright infringed by Posada? Explain.

_____

_____

_____

_____

9. While doing research for her college English class, Pena copied several pages from a library book on the library's copy machine without permission from the publisher. Did Pena violate the copyright law? Why or why not?

_____

_____

_____

_____

10. Kupid Kandy Kompany had manufactured and sold a very popular "Kupid" lollipop during the valentine season for over thirty years. A newly-established company began putting the name "Kupid" on its lollipops, claiming it could do so because Kupid Kandy Kompany had never obtained a federal or state trademark for its lollipop. How can Kupid Kandy Kompany protect itself?

_____

_____

_____

_____

Chapter 22   Bailments

Chapter Outline

22-1   Bailments of Personal Property

A bailment is the _____

_____

_____

22-2   Principal Types of Bailments

A. The principal types of bailments are:

1. _____

2. _____

3. _____

B. A consignment contract is _____

_____

_____

22-3   Burden of Proof

Most courts today shift the burden of proof in bailment cases to _____

_____

_____

22-4   Special Bailments

A. An innkeeper has an obligation to accept _____

_____

_____

1. The Civil Rights Act of 1964 prohibits _____

_____

_____

2. People may be turned away when _____

_____

_____

B. Innkeepers must respect their guests' _____

_____

C. Innkeepers have a greater duty of care toward their guests' property than_____

_____

D. Innkeepers have a lien on_____

_____

E. Credit card blocking is a common method used by hotels to _____

_____

_____

F. The Transportation Security Administration protects _____

_____

G. The Department of Homeland Security oversees_____

_____

_____

H. Like hotels, common carriers cannot _____

_____

I. Common carriers are liable as insurers of goods except in the case of

    1. _____

    2. _____

    3. _____

    4. _____

    5. _____

J. Common carriers may refuse goods that

    1. _____

    2. _____

    3. _____

    4. _____

    5. _____

K. Since 9/11, the FAA has established regulations that require _____

_____

_____

L. Common carriers may refuse passengers

    1. _____

    2. _____

    3. _____

M. Racial profiling may not be _____

_____

_____

N. Airline passengers who are eligible for denied boarding
compensation must be offered _____

_____

O. For travel wholly within the United States, the maximum liability of
an airline for lost luggage is_____

_____

P. Since 9/11, passengers may not carry on board such things as _____

_____

_____

Q. When goods are stored in a warehouse, the relationship _____

_____

_____

R. A warehouser must use that amount of care that _____

_____

_____

S. A warehouser's lien is _____

_____

_____

Legal Concepts

For each statement, write **T** *in the answer column if the statement is true* **Answer**
or **F** *if the statement is false.*

1. Borrowing a friend's car is an example of a bailment. 1. _____
2. It is a bailment when someone loans goods to another with the intention that the goods may be used and later replaced with an equal amount of different goods. 2. _____
3. In a bailment for the sole benefit of the bailor, the bailee owes a duty to use only slight care. 3. _____
4. In a bailment for the sole benefit of the bailee, any ordinary and expected expenses incurred in the use of another's property must be borne by the bailee. 4. _____
5. In a consignment contract, the consignor forwards the proceeds to the consignee less a fee. 5. _____
6. Today, when items in the possession of a bailee are damaged, lost, or stolen, the burden is on the bailor to prove that the bailee was negligent. 6. _____
7. It is illegal for hotels to use credit card blocking to secure payment for a room. 7. _____
8. With exceptions, innkeepers are held by law to be insurers of their guests' property. 8. _____
9. The Department of Homeland Security oversees the Coast Guard, the Customs Service, the Immigration and Naturalization Service, and the Transportation Security Administration. 9. _____
10. Common carriers of goods are insurers of all goods accepted for shipment. 10. _____
11. Passengers who do not consent to airport screening cannot be refused transportation. 11. _____
12. A person who is intoxicated, infected with a disease, or who might be inimical to safety may be refused transportation. 12. _____
13. Passengers who are bumped may receive compensation if they arrive more than one hour late at their destination. 13. _____

14. Banned items that are left at airline security checkpoints must be returned to their owners.

14. _____

15. If goods are not removed from a warehouse at the end of a storage period, the warehouser may sell them after giving proper notice.

15. _____

Language of the Law

Select the legal term that best matches each definition.

a. bailee
b. bailment
c. bailment for the sole benefit of the bailee
d. bailment for the sole benefit of the bailor

e. bailor
f. bill of lading
g. common carrier
h. consignee
i. consignor
j. mutual-benefit bailment

k. mutuum
l. racial profiling
m. warehouser
n. warehouse receipt
o. warehouser's lien

Answer

1. A person who entrusts goods to another for the purpose of selling them

1. _____

2. The act of targeting a person for criminal investigation because of ethnic characteristics

2. _____

3. A transaction in which borrowed goods are replaced with an equal quantity of the same goods

3. _____

4. The owner of the property involved in a bailment

4. _____

5. A receipt issued by a party engaged in the business of storing goods for hire

5. _____

6. The right to retain possession of warehoused goods until satisfaction of the charges imposed upon them

6. _____

7. A person engaged in the business of storing goods for hire

7. _____

8. A type of bailment in which the bailee is required to use great care

8. _____

9. The written contract between a common carrier and a shipper

9. _____

10. A carrier that holds itself out to the general public to provide transportation for compensation

10. _____

Applying the Law

1. Surhoff forgot to remove his jackknife from his key ring before arriving at an airport checkpoint, and it was confiscated. What obligation does the airport authority have for returning banned items that are left at security checkpoints?

_____

_____

_____

_____

2. Roberts borrowed two cups of flour from her neighbor to bake a cake for the company she was expecting. She bought five pounds of flour the next time she went grocery shopping and returned the two cups she had borrowed. Why was the borrowing of the flour not a bailment? What is the legal name of the transaction?

_____

_____

_____

_____

3. Reliable Shipping Co. was transporting a load of furniture from New York to Florida when a tornado that had spun off from a hurricane wrecked the truck and demolished its contents. Was Reliable Shipping Co. liable for the damage to the furniture? Why or why not?

_____

_____

_____

_____

4. Mueller attended the Army-Navy football game in Philadelphia. Kovich loaned Mueller a pair of binoculars to make the game more interesting. The binoculars were stolen when Mueller left them on a vacant seat during halftime. Was Mueller liable for damages for the loss? Give a reason for your answer.

_____

_____

_____

_____

5. Kinkaid asked permission to put a car in Anderson's two-car garage during a heavy snowstorm. After Kinkaid put the car in, Anderson locked the garage door, taking the key into the house. Kinkaid's car was stolen from the garage, but Anderson's was left untouched by the thieves. Was Anderson liable to Kinkaid for the loss of the car? Explain.

_____

_____

_____

_____

6. Harris rented a boat from Dukes for a trip to an island located two miles offshore. Since it was a good day for sailing, Harris continued the trip fifty miles farther across the bay. During that part of the trip, the boat struck a submerged piling, ripping out the bottom and ruining the craft. Harris proved in court that the accident did not result from any lack of care nor was it caused by any negligent act. Was Harris responsible to Dukes for the loss? Why or why not?

_____

_____

_____

_____

7. McKay picked up the goods that he had stored in Dexter's warehouse, promising to pay Dexter the following week. Several months passed, and McKay still had not paid Dexter for storing the goods. Dexter claimed that he had a warehouser's lien on the goods that were stored in his warehouse. Was Dexter correct? Explain.

_____

_____

_____

_____

8. Haskell checked luggage at the reservetions counter on East-West Airlines. The luggage contained a $3,500 notebook computer. Upon arrival in St. Louis, she presented the baggage check. An airline attendant could not find the luggage. Was East-West Airlines liable to Haskell? If so, for how much money?

_____

_____

_____

_____

9. Perez, who had made reservations six months in advance, was told when she arrived at the airport that she had been bumped. The airline agent told her that the airlines had asked for volunteers to give up their reservations but no one had done so; thus, Perez had no recourse. Was the airline agent correct? Explain.

_____

_____

_____

_____

10. Ohio and Western Railroad, a common carrier, accepted goods for shipment to the Keen Company in Illinois. Freight charges were to be collected from Keen. Keen demanded the goods without payment of the charges. Did the railroad have to accede to Keen's demands? Why or why not?

_____

_____

_____

_____

Chapter 23   Real Property

Chapter Outline

23-1   The Nature of Real Property

A. Landowners now own the airspace up to as high as _____
_____

B. Under the riparian rights doctrine, landowners_____
_____
_____
_____

C. Under the prior appropriations doctrine, the first person _____
_____
_____
_____

D. In deciding whether or not an item is a fixture, the courts ask
  1. _____
  2. _____
  3. _____
  4. _____

23-2   Easements

A. Easements are used to give people the right to _____
_____

B. An easement may be created
  1. _____
  _____
  2. _____
  _____
  3. _____
  _____

C. An easement by prescription is _____
_____
_____
_____

23-3   Estates in Real Property

A. The holder of an estate in fee simple has
_____
_____

B. A life estate may be created

    1. _____

       _____

    2. _____

       _____

    3. _____

       _____

23-4 Co-Ownership of Real Property

A. When a tenant in common dies, his or her share passes _____

_____

B. Four unities required to create a joint tenancy are

    1. _____

    2. _____

    3. _____

    4. _____

C. Upon the death of one joint tenant, the entire ownership _____

_____

D. Community property laws operate on the theory that _____

_____

E. A tenancy by the entirety may be held only by _____

_____

F. A tenancy in partnership is governed by _____

_____

23-5 Methods of Acquiring Title to Real Property

A. Title to real property may be acquired by _____

_____

_____

B. Types of deeds

    1. A general warranty deed guarantees _____

    _____

    2. A special warranty deed guarantees _____

    _____

    3. A bargain-and-sale deed is one that _____

    _____

    4. A quitclaim deed is one that _____

    _____

C. When people die owning real property solely, title passes _____

_____

D. To establish adverse possession, claimants must prove

1. _____

2. _____

3. _____

4. _____

23-6 Zoning Laws

Zoning laws protect against _____

_____

_____

23-7 Eminent Domain

A. Eminent domain is the right of federal, state, and local governments, or other public bodies, to _____

_____

_____

B. In 2005, the U.S. Supreme Court held that _____

_____

_____

C. Within two years after the Supreme Court's unpopular decision, more than 80 percent of U.S. states _____

_____

_____

Legal Concepts

For each statement, write **T** *in the answer column if the statement is true or* **F** *if the statement is false.*

Answer

1. Real property does not include perennial plants.

   1. _____

2. Someone who owns land has the right to cut off trespassing tree branches and roots that intrude into that land from another person's property.

   2. _____

3. Air rights are valuable and sometimes become a tax source for the government.

   3. _____

4. If a stream is navigable, the owner on each side owns from his or her bank to the center of the stream.

   4. _____

5. A built-in stove and an under-the-counter dishwasher are considered personal property.

   5. _____

6. Once an easement is created, it is bought and sold with the land.

   6. _____

7. Community property includes gifts and inheritances.

   7. _____

8. The most common form of ownership of real property is a life estate.

   8. _____

9. When two or more people own real property as tenants in common, one cotenant's interest is always the same as each of the other cotenants' interests.

9. _____

10. Upon the death of one of the parties who own real property as tenants by the entirety, no administration of the estate is necessary to give clear title to the survivor.

10. _____

11. A deed becomes effective when it is delivered by the grantee to the grantor.

11. _____

12. A quitclaim deed is the most desirable form of deed from the point of view of the grantee.

12. _____

13. When someone dies with a will, title to their real property passes to the persons named in the will without the use of a deed.

13. _____

14. Newly passed zoning laws do not apply to existing uses of the land.

14. _____

15. Zoning laws help to keep property values from declining and protect against the undesirable use of neighboring property.

15. _____

Language of the Law

Select the legal term that best matches each definition.

a. adverse possession
b. community property
c. cotenants
d. easement
e. eminent domain

f. grantee
g. grantor
h. life estate
i. quitclaim deed
j. real property

k. riparian owners
l. special warranty deed
m. tenancy by the entirety
n. tenants in common
o. variance

Answer

1. A deed that transfers to the buyer only the interest that the seller may have in a property

1. _____

2. An exemption or an exception permitting a use of property that differs from the uses permitted under the existing zoning ordinance

2. _____

3. The right of federal, state, and local governments to take private lands for public use by compensating the owners for the land taken

3. _____

4. The ground and everything permanently attached to it

4. _____

5. People who own land along the bank of a river or stream

5. _____

6. The right of a landowner to use the real property of another in a limited way

6. _____

7. A deed that can only be held by a husband and wife

7. _____

8. Property (except a gift or inheritance) that is acquired by the persona efforts of either spouse during marriage and which, by law, belongs to both spouses equally

8. _____

9. Ownership of real property for one's life or for the life of another

9. _____

10. The person to whom title in real property is transferred by deed

10. _____

Name_____ Date_____

Applying the Law

1. Cintron owned an ultralight airplane. She flew the plane 300 feet above the surface of some land owned by a neighbor, Diaz. When Diaz complained, Cintron argued that she was flying in the navigable air space. Was Cintron correct? Explain.

_____

_____

_____

_____

2. LaPlant owned a life estate in Stillwater Farm. When she moved to a nursing home, LaPlant said to her daughter, "You may stay at Stillwater Farm for as long as you live." Were LaPlant's instructions to her daughter accurate? Why or why not?

_____

_____

_____

3. Vargas owned, individually, a vacation cottage in the mountains. When Vargas died, his son, Andrew, inherited the property. Andrew claimed that he did not have good title because he had no deed to the property. Was Andrew correct? Explain.

_____

_____

_____

4. Waverly, whose house was situated behind Southwick's house, had a recorded easement to use a driveway through Southwick's land. When Waverly sold the house, Southwick tried to stop the new owner from using the driveway. Was Southwick successful in doing so? Explain.

_____

_____

_____

5. Oscar de la Renta, a physician who was married and lived in California, purchased a large farmhouse in his own name. His wife, Gloria, was a homemaker for her husband and three children. Because he used the money he earned as a physician to purchase the farmhouse, de la Renta considered that he owned a 100% interest in the property and that Gloria owned no interest in it. Was de la Renta correct? Why or why not?

_____

_____

_____

6. Richards's water supply came from an artesian well that had been drilled to a point 89 feet below the surface of his land. A nearby water company drilled wells to a much deeper depth on its property. Thousands of gallons of water were pumped out each day to provide water to buyers a mile away. Richards's well went dry because of the water company's lowering of the depth of available percolating waters. Can Richards stop the water company from lowering the water level? Why or why not?

_____

_____

_____

7. Starrett beautified a property by planting several hundred flower bulbs, shrubs, and perennials. The property was sold to Hawthorne. Before giving up possession, Starrett began digging out the bulbs and other plantings. It was her plan to move them all to a new home that she had bought. Could Hawthorne stop her from taking these plants? Why or why not?

_____

_____

_____

8. Foley, who lived in a state east of the Mississippi River, owned land through which Red Clay Creek flowed. Foley dammed up the creek and used all of the water to irrigate his field. Noonan, who lived downstream and was now without water, argued that she had a right to the use of the water from the creek. Was Noonan correct? Why or why not?

_____

_____

_____

9. Rheinhold and Kruger owned adjoining farms. The limbs of a large apple tree on Kruger's farm spread over Rheinhold's land, and its roots grew into Rheinhold's soil. Rheinhold cut off the limbs and the roots that extended onto his property. Could Kruger recover damages from Rheinhold in court? Explain.

_____

_____

_____

10. Picillo sold a vacant lot to Rodriquez. Picallo told Rodriquez that a special warranty deed was the most desirable form of deed. Was Picallo correct? Explain.

_____

_____

_____

Chapter 24   Landlord and Tenant

Chapter Outline

24-1 **The Landlord-Tenant Relationship**

The elements necessary for the creation of the landlord-tenant relation-ship are

A. _____

B. _____

C. _____

D. _____

E. _____

24-2 **Leasing Versus Other Relationships**

A. A lease differs from a license in that _____

_____

_____

B. A lodger is_____

_____

_____

24-3 **Types of Leasehold Interests**

A. A tenancy at will is _____

_____

_____

B. A tenancy for years is _____

_____

_____

C. A periodic tenancy is _____

_____

_____

D. A tenancy at sufferance arises_____

_____

_____

24-4 **The Lease Agreement**

A. The essential requirements of a lease are

1. _____

2. _____

3. _____

B. Rent controls limit_____

_____

_____

C. Security deposits protect _____

_____

_____

D. An option to renew gives _____

_____

_____

E. An option to purchase is _____

_____

_____

F. An assignment of a lease occurs when _____

_____

_____

24-5 Landlord's Duties

A. Landlords may not discriminate in selecting tenants on the grounds of _____

_____

_____

B. The warranty of habitability means _____

_____

C. The tenant is entitled to the exclusive _____

_____

D. A tenant who is wrongfully evicted _____

_____

_____

24-6 Tenant's Duties

A. A tenant has the duty to pay _____

_____

_____

B. A tenant has the duty to observe the valid _____

_____

_____

C. Unless agreed otherwise, the tenant must turn over to the landlord all _____

_____

_____

D. Tenants have a duty to avoid _____

_____

_____

24-7 Tort Liability

When a person is injured on leased property, the person usually responsible is _____

_____

24-8   Eviction Proceedings   Three methods available to landlords to regain possession of the property are

A. _____

B. _____

C. _____

Legal Concepts

For each statement, write **T** *in the answer column if the statement is true or* **F** *if the statement is false.*

Answer

1. There must be either an express or implied contract between the parties in the landlord-tenant relationship.

1. _____

2. The payment of rent by a tenant is essential to the creation of the landlord-tenant relationship.

2. _____

3. A lodger has the right to bring suit for trespass or to eject an intruder from the premises.

3. _____

4. A lease confers upon a tenant exclusive possession of the premises as against all the world.

4. _____

5. The granting of permission to hold a dance party in a hall is considered to be a lease of the hall.

5. _____

6. In most states a tenancy at will must be evidenced by a writing to satisfy the Statute of Frauds.

6. _____

7. A periodic tenancy ceases automatically upon the death of the tenant.

7. _____

8. A lease must contain a definite agreement as to the extent and bounds of the leased property.

8. _____

9. Many states now have laws, designed to protect tenants, that govern security deposits.

9. _____

10. A landlord may not discriminate in selecting tenants on the grounds of race, creed, color or sex.

10. _____

11. The warranty of habitability applies only to multiple-family dwellings.

11. _____

12. A landlord can never be prosecuted as a trespasser on his or her own rented property.

12. _____

13. A landlord has the right to remove, through court proceedings, a tenant for nonpayment of rent, disorderliness, or illegal use of the premises.

13. _____

14. Tenants may be held responsible for injuries to persons caused by defects in areas under the tenants' control.

14. _____

15. Unlawful detainer is a legal procedure that provides a tenant with a quick method for getting action against a landlord.

15. _____

Language of the Law

Select the legal term that best matches each definition.

a. actual eviction

b. constructive eviction

c. ejectment

d. eviction

e. landlord

f. lease

g. leasehold estate

h. lessee

i. lessor

j. lodger

k. periodic tenancy

l. quiet enjoyment

m. tenancy at sufferance

n. tenancy at will

o. tenancy for years

Answer

1. The common-law name for the lawsuit brought by a landlord to have a tenant evicted from the premises   1. _____

2. The situation that arises when a tenant is physically deprived of a leasehood   2. _____

3. Another name for the landlord who gives the lease to a tenant   3. _____

4. The right of a tenant to the undisturbed possession of the property leased   4. _____

5. A fixed-period tenancy that continues for successive periods until one of the parties terminates it by giving notice to the other party   5. _____

6. The agreement that gives rise to the landlord-tenant relationship   6. _____

7. An estate for a definite or fixed period of time   7. _____

8. Another name for a tenant   8. _____

9. The type of tenancy that arises when a tenant wrongfully remains in possession of the premises after expiration of the tenancy   9. _____

10. The situation that arises when a tenant is deprived of something that is of a substantial nature that was called for under the lease   10. _____

Applying the Law

1. Ying rented an apartment at the Bay View apartment building. During the winter, the owner of the building failed to remove the snow and ice from the steps leading to the main entrance of the building. A friend of Ying's slipped on the steps and injured her back. Was Ying responsible for the injuries? Why or why not?

_____

_____

_____

_____

2. While visiting Zelig's apartment, Keech slipped on a loose scatter rug and broke her arm. Zelig had placed the small scatter rug on a newly polished floor. Keech sued the owner of the apartment building for negligence. Would she win the case? Explain.

_____

_____

_____

_____

3. On October 15, Wright rented an apartment at the Superior Apartments building for a period of one year. After living there for a month, Wright discovered that the furnace was broken and that the apartment had no heat. Wright notified the landlord, but nothing was done to repair the furnace. When the temperature dropped to thirty-eight degrees, Wright moved out. The owner of the building sued Wright for the balance of the rent due for the year. Did Wright win the case? Why or why not?

_____

_____

_____

4. Ratcliff rented a cottage on Marilee Lake for one year under a periodic tenancy. One month after entering into the tenancy, Ratcliff died. Shortly thereafter, daughter, Shirley, moved into the cottage. The landlord brought suit to evict Shirley on the grounds that Ratcliff's death ended the tenancy. Did Shirley win the case? Explain.

_____

_____

_____

5. Denver Realty rented a house to Garcia under a periodic tenancy. Terms of the lease required her to inform the landlord ninety days prior to the end of the lease of her intention of terminating the leasehold. Garcia neglected to do so, moving to an apartment one weekend without warning and then failing to make lease payments to Denver. Did the lease come to an end when Garcia moved out? Why or why not?

_____

_____

_____

6. Pine Brook Apartments rented Heck an apartment for one year, requiring a security deposit of $700. The apartment manager refused to return Heck's deposit at the end of the leasehold, claiming the $700 would be used in preparing the apartment for the next tenant. Heck left no damage or excessive-use depreciation when he vacated the apartment. Did Pine Brook have the right to retain Heck's $700? Explain.

_____

_____

_____

7. Vargas's rented house was entered by the landlord during Vargas's absence and without his permission. The landlord customarily made periodic visits to rented properties to observe their condition. Vargas charged the landlord with trespassing. The lease contained no condition relating to landlord inspection. Was the landlord a trespasser? Why or why not?

_____

_____

_____

_____

8. While attending college away from home, Soroka boarded with a private family. She had her own room and received two meals each day. Was she considered to be a tenant? Explain.

_____

_____

_____

_____

9. Perry's one-year lease expired, but she refused to leave her apartment even though she was requested to by her landlord and was given proper notice. Her tender of rent for the first month of the next year was refused. She claimed that she was a tenant at will. Was she correct? Why or why not?

_____

_____

_____

_____

10. O'Brian rented a house from the American Fruit Farms Company during his employment as a seasonal worker with the company. After two months, his employment with the company was terminated, and the American Fruit Farms Company requested him to move out of the house immediately. O'Brian did not comply with the request, and the company sought to have him removed by court order. Would the court allow O'Brian to stay longer? Explain.

_____

_____

_____

_____

Chapter 25   Wills, Trusts, and Estates

Chapter Outline

25-1 **Sources and Relevance of Probate Law**

    A. The process of handling the will and the estate of a deceased person is called_____

_____

    B. It is necessary to check one's own state laws to ascertain the rules for writing a will and to determine how property passes when some someone dies because_____

_____

_____

    C. The subject of probate law is relevant to _____

_____

25-2 **Preliminary Matters and Probate Terminology**

    A. Three examples of advance directives are

       1. _____

       2. _____

       3. _____

    B. In states that have adopted the Uniform Probate Code, the term devise refers to _____

_____

25-3 **Dying With a Will**

    A. A will may be made by _____

_____

    B. In determining sound mind, the court asks

       1. _____

       2. _____

       3. _____

       4. _____

    C. With the exception of an oral will, a will must be _____

_____

    D. A will must be signed by _____

_____

    E. With the exception of some handwritten wills, a will must be witnessed by _____

_____

    F. In many states, persons and their spouses who witness a will may not _____

_____

G. In many states, witnesses are not required for _____

_____

_____

H. In some states, oral wills may be made by _____

_____

_____

I. Among the devices to protect surviving family members when a spouse dies are

    1. _____

    2. _____

    3. _____

J. A surviving spouse who does not like the provisions of a deceased spouse's will may _____

_____

K. Children left out of a will are protected if they can prove _____

_____

_____

L. Adopted children are given _____

_____

_____

M. A will may be revoked by

    1. _____

    2. _____

    3. _____

    4. _____

N. A will may be contested on the grounds of

    1. _____

    2. _____

    3. _____

25-4 Dying Without a Will

A. When people die without a will, their property passes to others according to _____

_____

B. Under a typical state statute, if a person dies intestate, the rights of a surviving spouse are

    1. _____

    2. _____

    3. _____

  C. The rights of other heirs are

    1. _____

    2. _____

    3. _____

  D. The property of a person who dies without a will goes to the state only when _____

   _____

25-5   **Simultaneous Death**

When two people die in a common disaster so that it is impossible to determine who died first, the _____

_____

25-6   **Settling an Estate**

When people die owning assets, their estates must be _____

_____

_____

25-7   **Trusts**

  A. In a trust, title is split between_____

   _____

  B. A testamentary trust is_____

   _____

  C. A living trust comes into existence _____

   _____

  D. The trustee is obligated by law to _____

   _____

Legal Concepts

For each statement, write **T** *in the answer column if the statement is true or* **F** *if the statement is false.*   **Answer**

1. The laws governing the writing of wills and the settling of estates are uniform throughout the United States.   **1.** _____

2. The subject of probate law is relevant to all forms of business entities.   **2.** _____

3. A living will is an oral expression of a person's wishes to die a natural death and not be kept alive by artificial means.   **3.** _____

4. A person of any age may make a will.   **4.** _____

5. Undue influence is a valid reason for a will to be declared invalid.   **5.** _____

6. When a person dies intestate, both real and personal property are distributed according to the laws of the state where the deceased was domiciled.   **6.** _____

7. A parent may not disinherit a child.   7. _____
8. Adopted children are given the same legal rights as natural
    children.   8. _____
9. Surviving spouses are not assured a share of their spouse's
    estate.   9. _____
10. A codicil must be executed with the same formalities as a will.   10. _____
11. All states treat holographic wills as valid.   11. _____
12. Those who receive real property under a will are known as
    legatees.   12. _____
13. Property is often placed in trust so that it will be preserved for
    future generations.   13. _____
14. The chief objection to a spray trust is that it gives the trustee
    too much control.   14. _____
15. A living trust is a trust that is created by will.   15. _____

Language of the Law

Select the legal term that best matches each definition.

a. Administrator	**f.** durable power of attorney	**k.** next of kin
b. advance directives	**g.** health care proxy	**l.** probate
c. bequest	**h.** heir	**m.** surety
d. codicil	**i.** intestate	**n.** testamentary trust
e. devise	**j.** living trust	**o.** testator

                                                                                                   Answer

1. A term given to the estate of someone who dies without having
    prepared a valid will   1. _____
2. A supplement to a will   2. _____
3. A document that authorizes another person to act on one's
    behalf either surviving incapacity or becoming effective upon
    incapacity   3. _____
4. Personal property that is left by will   4. _____
5. A trust that is created by will   5. _____
6. The procedure whereby an estate is managed and closed under
    the supervision of a court   6. _____
7. A person appointed to take charge of an estate when the
    deceased has left no will   7. _____
8. Real property that is left by a will   8. _____
9. Written statements in which people give instructions for future
    medical care if they become unable to do so themselves   9. _____
10. A trust that comes into existence while the settlor is alive   10. _____

Applying the Law

1. Lopez, angry at his wife, made a will leaving his entire estate to charity. Lopez specifically wrote in the will that he intended to leave his wife nothing. Can Lopez's wife receive anything from Lopez's estate? Explain.

_____

_____

_____

_____

2. Becket, a 16-year-old singing sensation known throughout the United States, made a will leaving his large estate to his sister Kathleen. Becket was killed in a plane crash. For what legal reason did Becket's parents inherit his estate rather than Kathleen?

_____

_____

_____

_____

3. Pierce's will left her estate in equal shares to a natural daughter, an adopted daughter, and two stepsons. The daughters claimed that the stepsons could not legally inherit from Pierce. Were the daughters correct? Why or why not?

_____

_____

_____

_____

4. Hauck signed a will in the presence of only one witness, leaving her entire estate to her friend, Brodie, and naming Caruso as executor. When Caruso died shortly thereafter, Hauck signed a codicil to the will in the presence of two witnesses, naming DiCarlo as executor. Hauck died. Did Brodie inherit her entire estate? Why or why not?

_____

_____

_____

_____

5. Thurber prepared a will without the assistance of an attorney. With all intent to leave his estate to his children, Thurber wrote, "I leave my real and personal property to my heirs." Why might Thurber's children not inherit the entire estate?

_____

_____

_____

_____

6. A short time before her death, Howell decided to remove the name of a former friend from among those to benefit from her estate. Howell blanked out the name and inserted another name in its place. Would the person whose name was newly inserted in the will inherit from Howell's estate? Why or why not?

_____

_____

_____

_____

7. Handy signed a will at the office of a bank. The bank president took the will to his office and had it witnessed by secretaries working in the office. Handy was not present at the time. In the event of a dispute after Handy's death, would the will be allowed? Explain.

_____

_____

_____

_____

8. Singh, a widow with two children, married DeFazio, a widower with one child. On their honeymoon in Italy, while riding on a train from Florence to Pisa, they were both killed instantly when their train collided head on with another train passing through a long, dark tunnel. Neither one had a will, and each owned property in their own name with nothing owed jointly. What law will govern the settlement of their estates? How will each person's separately-owned property be distributed?

_____

_____

_____

_____

9. Thornton lived alone, was very ill, and had no one to care for her. She was wealthy, but would not go to an attorney or engage a nurse because of her frugality. Thornton wrote a will in her own handwriting, signed her name, Elizabeth Thornton, and placed it among other papers in her family Bible. Why could this will be probated in certain states?

_____

_____

_____

_____

10. Chi was a successful inventor with many inventions and patents to his credit. He was self-trained, had never gone to school, and could neither read nor write. At an advanced age, he had an attorney prepare a will, which was signed with an X and witnessed by younger associates of the inventor. Would such a signature satisfy the demands of probate? Why or why not?

_____

_____

_____

_____

Chapter 26   Purpose and Types of Negotiable Instruments

Chapter Outline

26-1 Purpose of Negotiable Instruments

The purpose of negotiable instruments is to _____
_____
_____
_____

26-2 Promise Instruments

The two types of negotiable instruments that contain a promise to pay money are a _____ and a _____

A. A note is _____
_____

  1. A demand note is _____
  _____

  2. A time note is _____
  _____

  3. An installment note is _____
  _____

B. A certificate of deposit is _____
_____

  1. A CD is a note of _____
  _____

  2. CDs are written for a specific_____
  _____

  3. Banks pay higher interest for CDs than for regular savings accounts because_____
  _____
  _____

The two types of negotiable instruments that contain an order to pay are _____ and _____

26-3 Order Instruments

A. draft is _____
_____

B. When a draft is presented for payment, the drawee may _____
_____

C. A sight draft is_____
_____

D. A time draft is _____
_____

E. A draft that is drawn in one country but payable in another is called

_____

_____

F. A check is _____

_____

_____

G. A certified check is _____

_____

_____

H. When a check is certified, the drawer is _____

_____

I. Special checks include the following
   1. A bank draft is _____

_____

   2. A cashier's check is _____

_____

   3. Traveler's checks are _____

_____

   4. A money order is _____

_____

26-4   **Parties to Negotiable Instruments**

A. A maker is _____

_____

_____

B. Comakers are _____

_____

_____

C. An issuer is _____

_____

_____

D. A drawer is _____

_____

_____

E. A drawee is _____

_____

_____

F. A payee is _____

_____

_____

G. A bearer is _____

_____

_____

H. A holder is_____

_____

_____

I. A holder in due course is_____

_____

_____

J. An indorser is _____

_____

_____

K. An indorsee is _____

_____

_____

L. An acceptor is _____

_____

_____

26-5 **Requirements of Negotiable Interests**

A. To be negotiable, an instrument must:

1. _____

2. _____

3. _____

4. _____

5. _____

6. _____

B. The omission of the date_____

_____

_____

Legal Concepts

For each statement, write **T** *in the answer column if the statement is true or* **F** *if the statement is false.*   **Answer**

1. The two types of negotiable instruments that contain a promise to pay money are notes and drafts.   **1.** _____

2. A holder of a demand note may decide to collect the balance due at any time and for any reason.   **2.** _____

3. A CD is a note of the bank.   **3.** _____

4. In contrast to notes, which are orders to pay money, drafts are promises to pay money.   4. _____

5. If the drawee refuses to pay an unaccepted draft, the draft is dishonored, and the drawee is liable for refusing to pay it.   5. _____

6. An acceptance must be written on the draft itself; it may not be written on a separate piece of paper.   6. _____

7. A draft that is payable "thirty days after sight" is an example of a sight draft.   7. _____

8. A check is the most common form of draft.   8. _____

9. A cashier's check is a check drawn by a bank upon itself.   9. _____

10. Under the UCC, a *bank* money order is a check and payment can be stopped on it like an ordinary check.   10. _____

11. When a check is certified, the drawer is discharged regardless of when it was done or who obtained the acceptance.   11. _____

12. A writing that says "IOU $500" is negotiable.   12. _____

13. An instrument payable when a person marries is negotiable.   13. _____

14. Negotiable instruments, except for checks, must be payable to order or to bearer.   14. _____

15. The omission of the date affects the negotiability of an instrument.   15. _____

Language of the Law

Select the legal term that best matches each definition.

a. acceptor	f. draft	k. installment note
b. bearer	g. drawee	l. maker
c. certificate of deposit	h. drawer	m. payee
d. check	i. holder	n. sight draft
e. demand note	j. indorser	o. time draft

                                                   Answer

1. The person to whom a negotiable instrument is made payable   1. _____

2. A drawee of a draft who has promised to honor the draft is presented by signing it on its face   2. _____

3. An order instrument through which the person writing it orders another person to pay money to a third person   3. _____

4. A written order on the drawee to pay on demand the amount named in the instrument   4. _____

5. The person on whom a draft or check is drawn   5. _____

6. The person in physical possession of a commercial paper indorsed in blank or payable to bearer   6. _____

7. The person who creates a draft or check by writing it   7. _____

8. The person who makes and signs a promise instrument such as a promissory note   8. _____

9. An ordinary note in which the principal is payable in a series of payments at specified times

9. _____

10. A draft drawn on a bank and payable on demand

10. _____

Applying the Law

1. Pierce gave the following instrument to Jones: "On demand, I promise to pay to the order of Charles E. Jones $5,000. [signed] Charles Pierce." The next day, Jones was involved in a car accident and needed money to buy a car. He demanded the $5,000 from Pierce. Pierce refused to pay, arguing that the note was not due for a year. Was Pierce correct? Why or why not?

_____
_____
_____
_____

2. While walking along a sidewalk, Giron found an uncashed check that was payable to the order of Luciano P. Mancuso. Giron took the check to a bank, claiming that he was a bearer of the instrument. Do you agree with Giron? Why or why not?

_____
_____
_____
_____

3. In No. 3 (above), what would have had to be done to cause Giron to be a holder of the check?

_____
_____
_____
_____

4. In No. 3 (above), was the check negotiated to Giron? Why or why not?

_____
_____
_____
_____

5. In No. 3 (above), was the check order paper or bearer paper? Explain.

_____

_____

_____

6. "December 5, 20—, Albuquerque, New Mexico. Two years after date, pay to the order of Xavier Monaco, $500 with interest. [Signed] Monte Miranda. To: Leon Sloboda, 29 Caballo Avenue, Las Cruces, New Mexico." Was this instrument a draft? Explain.

_____

_____

_____

7. While browsing through Salt's antique shop in Georgetown, Massachusetts, a tourist from Mexico found a chair that he wanted to buy. The price was $600. Since the tourist was short of money, Salt agreed to take $400 in cash and the balance in a promissory note. The tourist made the note payable to the order of Salt in the amount of 458,000 Mexican pesos. Later, Salt showed the note to a friend, who said that it was not negotiable. Was the friend correct? Explain.

_____

_____

_____

8. The next day, the same tourist returned to Salt's antique shop to ask a question about the chair he had purchased. Salt gave back the note that the tourist had given him the day before in exchange for a note payable to his order in the amount of "$200 worth of silver." Was the new note negotiable? Why or why not?

_____

_____

_____

9. "October 17, 20—, Winchester, Massachusetts. Eighteen months after date, I promise to pay to the order of Margaret Otis, $1,000 with interest. Given in payment of merchandise. [Signed] Henry Mohr." Was this instrument negotiable? Why or why not?

_____

_____

_____

10. Streeter gave her daughter the following instrument: "September 1, 20—, Due Jeanne Streeter $1,000, when she is eighteen years old. [Signed] Edna Streeter." Jeanne Streeter, the payee, attempted to negotiate the instrument to a bank. The bank refused to take it, saying that it was not negotiable. Was the bank correct? Explain.

_____

_____

_____

Chapter 27   Transferring Negotiable Instruments

Chapter Outline

27-1 **Transferring Instruments**

 A. An instrument is issued when _____ _____ _____

 B. An instrument is transferred when _____ _____ _____

 C. An assignment is _____ _____ _____

 D. Negotiation is the transfer_____ _____ _____

  1. To be negotiated, order paper must be _____ _____

  2. Bearer paper may be negotiated by _____ _____

27-2 **The Concept of Negotiability**

 A. When an instrument is transferred by negotiation, the person receiving it is provided _____ _____

 B. Instruments that do not meet all of the requirements of negotiability cannot_____ _____

27-3 **Negotiation by Indorsement**

 A. An instrument is indorsed when _____ _____ _____

 B. Indorsements may be written _____ _____

 C. Under Regulation CC,_____ _____

 D. A blank indorsement consists of_____ _____

E. A special indorsement is made by _____

_____

F. A restrictive indorsement limits the _____

_____

G. A qualified indorsement is one in which _____

_____

27-4   **Obligations of Indorsers**

A. An indorser who receives consideration for an instrument warrants that

     1. _____

     2. _____

     3. _____

     4. _____

     5. _____

B. Unless an indorsement states otherwise, every indorser agrees ___

_____

_____

27-5   **Multiple Payees, Missing and Forged Indorsements**

A. If an instrument is payable to either of two payees, _____

_____

_____

B. If an instrument is payable to both of two payees, _____

_____

_____

C. A bank that has taken an instrument to send through the collection process may supply _____

_____

D. With three exceptions and, unless ratified, an unauthorized or forged signature _____

_____

E. The exceptions are

     1. _____

        _____

     2. _____

        _____

     3. _____

        _____

Legal Concepts

For each statement, write **T** *in the answer column if the statement is true or* **F** *if the statement is false.*

1. Instruments may be transferred only by negotiation. 1. _____

2. A negotiable instrument is assigned when a person whose indorsement is required on it transfers it without indorsing it. 2. _____

3. A negotiation is the transfer of an instrument in such form that the transferee becomes a holder. 3. _____

4. The concept of negotiability is one of the most important features of negotiable instruments. 4. _____

5. When an instrument is transferred by negotiation, the transferee may receive greater rights than the transferor had. 5. _____

6. Indorsements may be written in ink, typed or rubber stamped. 6. _____

7. The Uniform Commercial Code (UCC) requires that indorsements be placed on the back of instruments. 7. _____

8. An instrument that is indorsed with a special indorsement must be indorsed by the indorsee before it can be further negotiated. 8. _____

9. When an instrument is indorsed in blank, it becomes payable to bearer and may be transferred by delivery alone. 9. _____

10. An indorser who receives consideration for an instrument warrants that all signatures are authentic and authorized. 10. _____

11. A qualified indorser warrants that the instrument is not subject to a defense of any party which can be asserted against the indorser. 11. _____

12. Unless an indorsement states otherwise, every indorser agrees to pay any subsequent holder the face amount of the instrument if it is dishonored. 12. _____

13. When an instrument is dishonored, indorsers have no obligation where proper presentment has been made and notice of dishonor has been given to them. 13. _____

14. An instrument payable to either of two payees, as in, "Pay to the order of B. Bell *or* R. Alt," requires the indorsement of both payees to be negotiated. 14. _____

15. The burden of preventing padded payrolls is on the drawer of payroll checks. 15. _____

Language of the Law

Select the legal term that best matches each definition.

a. *Allonge*
b. assignment
c. bearer paper
d. blank indorsement
e. conditional indorsement

f. conversion
g. dishonored
h. indorsee
i. indorsement in full
j. negotiation

k. order paper
l. qualified indorsement
m. restrictive indorsement
n. special indorsement
o. without recourse

	Answer
1. Another name for an indorsement in full	1. _____
2. An indorsement in which no particular indorsee is specified	2. _____
3. The transfer of a contract right from one person to another	3. _____
4. Not paid by the maker or drawee	4. _____
5. The wrongful exercise of dominion and control over another's personal property	5. _____
6. An indorsement that limits the rights of the indorsee in some manner in order to protect the rights of the indorser	6. _____
7. A person to whom a negotiable instrument is transferred by indorsement	7. _____
8. An indorsement in which the words *without recourse* are used	8. _____
9. Another name for a rider attached to a negotiable instrument	9. _____
10. An indorsement that makes the rights of the indorsee subject to the happening of a certain event or condition	10. _____

Applying the Law

1. Allen wrote a check to Brown for $300 in payment for a used laptop computer. Without indorsing the check, Brown gave it to his friend Carol in payment for an earlier loan. Was the transfer of the check to Carol a negotiation? Why or why not?

_____

_____

_____

_____

2. Allen wrote another check to David for $100 in payment for a used printer. indorsed the check in blank and gave it to Earnest in exchange for two tickets to a baseball game. Was the transfer of the check to Earnest a negotiation? Explain.

_____

_____

_____

_____

3. Earnest, in the above case, gave the check without indorsing it, to Frank in exchange for two tickets to a football game. Frank indorsed the check, "Pay to Second National Bank for deposit only" and mailed it to the bank. Was the transfer of the check to Frank a negotiation to the bank? Explain?

_____

_____

_____

_____

4. If David in Number 2 above had indorsed the check with a special indorsement instead of a blank indorsement, what would Earnest have had to have done to negotiate the instrument?

_____

_____

_____

_____

5. (a) Was Carol a holder in Number 1 above? (b) Was Earnest a holder in Number 2 above? (c) Was Frank a holder in Number 3 above? Give reasons for your answers.

_____

_____

_____

_____

6. When Fielding received his paycheck, he indorsed it in blank, placed it on his desk, and went to get a cup of coffee. The check accidentally blew out an open window. Curren, a stranger to Fielding, found the check on the sidewalk below, took it to a bank, and cashed it. Was the transfer of the check to the bank a negotiation? Why or why not?

_____

_____

_____

_____

7. When Hernandez received her paycheck, she indorsed it with a restrictive indorsement, placed it in an envelope with a deposit slip, and mailed it to the bank for deposit to her account. Why was the restrictive indorsement a good one to use for this transaction?

_____

_____

_____

_____

8. Coughlin was an indorser on a check. A subsequent holder presented the check to the bank named on the instrument and was informed that the drawer did not have an account at the bank. Coughlin, as an indorser, was called upon for payment of the check. Must Coughlin pay the subsequent holder of the instrument? Explain.

_____

_____

_____

_____

9. LeVander forged the signature of Gore to a note which she negotiated to Burns for value. Burns then indorsed and delivered the note to Gossett as a down payment on a used car. When Gossett presented the note to Gore for payment, the forgery was recognized. Gossett demanded payment from Burns. Burns claimed innocence of any knowledge of the forgery and therefore freedom from liability. Would a court rule for Gossett in an action against Burns? Why or why not?

_____

_____

_____

_____

10. Raughley indorsed a check as follows: "John R. Raughley, without recourse." The check was subsequently found to have been raised from $90 to $900. A later holder claimed that Raughley was liable on the instrument, since it was not honored by the bank because of the alteration. Raughley denied liability on the basis of the qualified indorsement he had used. Did the qualified indorsement allow Raughley to avoid liability for payment of the check? Explain.

_____

_____

_____

_____

Chapter 28   Holders in Due Course, Defenses, and Liabilities

Chapter Outline

28-1   **Holder in Due Course**

A. People who are holders in due course of negotiable instruments can receive _____

_____

B. A holder in due course is _____

_____

_____

C. A holder is someone who is in possession of an instrument that is _____

_____

D. People give value for an instrument when _____

_____

_____

E. Good faith means _____

_____

F. A holder has notice that a demand instrument is overdue when _____

_____

_____

G. A holder who receives an instrument from a holder in due course acquires _____

_____

28-2   **Personal Defenses**

A. Personal defenses are defenses that cannot be used against _____

_____

B. The most common personal defenses are

1. _____

2. _____

3. _____

4. _____

5. _____

6. _____

28-3   **Real Defenses**

A. Real defenses can be used against _____

_____

_____

B. The following are real defenses:

1. _____
2. _____
3. _____
4. _____
5. _____
6. _____

28-4 Liability of the Parties

A. No person is liable on an instrument unless _____
_____

B. The following are obligated to pay an instrument without reservations of any kind:

1. _____
2. _____
3. _____

C. The drawer of a draft that has not been accepted is obligated _____
_____
_____

D. If a bank accepts a draft, the drawer is _____
_____

E. If a drawee other than a bank accepts a draft and it is later dishonored, the obligation of the drawer is _____
_____

F. Indorsers are obligated to pay an instrument only when the following conditions are met:

1. _____
2. _____
3. _____

G. Presentment may be made by _____
_____

H. Dishonor means _____
_____

I. Notice of dishonor may be given by any _____
_____
_____

Legal Concepts

For each statement, write **T** *in the answer column if the statement is true or* **F** *if the statement is false.*

Answer

1. Holders in due course receive more rights than other parties.

1. _____

2. To be a holder in due course, the holder must take an instrument in good faith.

2. _____

3. If an instrument is transferred to a person as a gift, that person would not qualify as a holder in due course.

3. _____

4. People do not give value for instruments when they accept instruments in payment of debts.

4. _____

5. An individual who is on notice that an instrument is overdue may be a holder in due course.

5. _____

6. A check is overdue sixty days after its date.

6. _____

7. A holder who receives title to an instrument from someone who is a holder in due course receives all the rights of the holder in due course.

7. _____

8. Personal defenses are defenses that can be used against a holder in due course.

8. _____

9. Lack of consideration is a defense that may not be used against a holder in due course.

9. _____

10. The defense of fraud in the inducement may be used against a holder in due course.

10. _____

11. An instrument that is associated with an illegal act is not collectible by anyone, not even a holder in due course.

11. _____

12. No person is liable on an instrument unless that person's signature appears thereon or is written by an authorized agent.

12. _____

13. The maker of a promissory note is obligated to pay without reservations.

13. _____

14. If a bank accepts a draft that is later dishonored, the obligation of the drawer is the same as an indorser.

14. _____

15. Notice of dishonor of an instrument must be given in writing to the drawer and the indorsers.

15. _____

Language of the Law

Select the legal term that best matches each definition.

a. delivery
b. failure of consideration
c. fraud as to the essential nature of the transaction
d. good faith
e. holder

f. holder in due course
g. holder in due course rule
h. lack of consideration
i. limited defense
j. personal defense

k. presentment
l. protest
m. real defense
n. shelter provision
o. universal defense

1. Honest in fact

2. Holders of consumer credit contracts who are holders in due course are subject to personal defenses

3. A rule allowing a holder who receives an instrument from a holder in due course to receive all the rights of the former party

4. A holder who takes an instrument for value, in good faith, and without notice that it is overdue or has been dishonored

5. A demand made by a holder to pay or accept an instrument

6. A defense that may be used when no consideration existed in the underlying contract for which the instrument was issued

7. A defense that may not be used against a holder in due course

8. A person who is in possession of a negotiable instrument that is issued or indorsed to that person's order or to bearer

9. A defense that may be used when the other party breaches the contract by not furnishing the agreed consideration nature of the transaction

10. Another name for a universal defense

Answer

1. _____

2. _____

3. _____

4. _____

5. _____

6. _____

7. _____

8. _____

9. _____

10. _____

Applying the Law

1. Schultz found a check on the sidewalk that was payable to the order of Tyronne Johnson in the amount of $450. Schultz indorsed his own name on the check and cashed it at a bank. Was the bank a holder in due course of the check? Why or why not?

_____

_____

_____

_____

2. Tarrant wrote a check payable to the order of his daughter, Jessica, in the amount of $100 and gave it to her as a birthday gift. Was Jessica a holder in due course of the instrument? Why or why not?

_____

_____

_____

3. Jessica Tarrant indorsed the $100 check that she had received as a gift from her father with a special indorsement and gave it to Watson in payment for a used camcorder. Watson indorsed the check in blank and gave it to his son, Cody, as a gift. Did Cody have the rights of a holder in due course? Explain.

_____

_____

_____

_____

4. Watney misplaced a check that she had received for helping to decorate some-one's house. She found the check four months later and cashed it at a local grocery store. For what reason was the grocery store not a holder in due course of the check?

_____

_____

_____

_____

5. Garber, a minor, purchased a used car for $1,500 from a car dealer. In payment, she gave $500 in cash and a promissory note for the balance to be paid in three months. The dealer indorsed the note and negotiated it to a bank. A week later, Garber demolished the car in an accident. Must Garber pay the amount of the note to the bank when it is due? Why or why not?

_____

_____

_____

_____

6. Creedon was employed as a maintenance worker by Weaver Realty Co. While cleaning an office, Creedon found a paper on which an officer of Weaver Realty had written her signature. Creedon executed a note payable thirty days after sight above the signature and negotiated the instrument by indorsement to an acquaintance for value. When the note was presented for payment, the Weaver Realty officer refused to pay. Did the holder have rights against the alleged maker of the note? Explain.

_____

_____

_____

_____

7. Moynihan executed and left on her desk a promissory note made out to Pappas. Moynihan owed Pappas the money specified on the note for her purchase of a lawn tractor a week previously. Pappas was admitted to Moynihan's office, saw the note made out to her, picked it up, and departed without seeing Moynihan. Pappas negotiated the note to her bank through indorsement and delivery. When the bank presented the note for payment, Moynihan refused, claiming she had not delivered the note to the indorser. Did Moynihan have a defense against the bank? Why or why not?

_____

_____

_____

_____

8. Crenshaw bought a tool set from National Supply Co. and signed a consumer credit contract agreeing to pay the amount of $798 in twelve monthly installments. National Supply Co. had an arrangement with Ace Finance Company to finance National's customers' purchases and immediately negotiated the credit contract to Ace in exchange for payment. The tool set turned out to be defective. Could Crenshaw use the defense of a defective tool set (a personal defense) if he is sued by Ace Finance Company for the money owed? Why or why not?

_____

_____

_____

_____

9. Washington accepted for value, by indorsement from a holder in due course, a check that had been altered from an original amount of $75 to $750. After investigation, it was learned that the drawer of the check had not taken the usual and ordinary precautions in drawing the check, thus making the alteration possible. The drawer contended that he was not liable for the $750, but only for the original amount, $75, for which the check was drawn. Was the drawer's contention correct? Why or why not?

_____

_____

_____

10. McDougal executed and delivered a ninety-day note for $3,000 payable to bearer and dated August 22, 20—. Someone erased the date and wrote in ink the words "December 19, 20—" over the erasure. The alternation was obvious to anyone who examined the note. Why can't someone who purchases the note after the alteration be a holder in due course?

_____

_____

_____

Chapter 29   Bank-Depositor Relationships, Deposits, and Collections

Chapter Outline

29-1   The Bank-Depositor Relationship

A. The drawee bank is under a duty to honor _____
_____
_____

B. The bank is under no obligation to a customer to pay a _____
_____

C. After the death of the drawer, a bank may pay or certify checks for
_____
_____

D. If a bank, in good faith, pays an altered amount to a holder, it
may deduct from the drawer's account only_____
_____
_____

E. Funds from checks drawn on
   1. the U.S. Treasury, or any state or local government, and any
   bank draft must be made available _____
   _____

   2. banks within the same Federal Reserve district must be made
   available _____
   _____

   3. banks outside the bank's Federal Reserve district must be
   made available _____
   _____

F. Payor banks are required to either settle or return checks _____
_____

G. Depositors owe a duty to banks in which they have checking
accounts to_____
_____

H. Most states have statutes making it larceny or attempted larceny for
_____
_____

I. The UCC imposes a duty on depositors to _____
_____
_____

J. Stop-payment orders are binding on the bank _____

_____

    1. if oral for _____

    2. if in writing for _____

K. The right of a bank to substitute itself for another is called_____

_____

L. The basic FDIC insurance protects individual bank accounts for up to _____

_____

29-2   **Electronic Banking**

A. Four advantages of using electronic banking are:

    1. _____

    2. _____

    3. _____

    4. _____

B. An ATM card is used together with_____

_____

C. Debit cards are used to _____

_____

D. A debit card offers less protection than a credit card in two ways:

    1. _____

    2. _____

E. Regulation E issued by the Federal Reserve Board under the Electronic Fund Transfer Act establishes _____

_____

_____

29-3   **Bank Deposits and Collections**

A. Terms to describe banks are as follows:

    1. _____

    2. _____

    3. _____

    4. _____

    5. _____

B. The life cycle of a check begins_____

_____

_____

C. Prior to 2004, electronic check processing could not be used because_____

_____

_____

D. The Check 21 Act established a new negotiable instrument called a substitute check, which is _____

_____

E. Banks that use substitute checks make the following warranties:

   1. _____

   2. _____

   3. _____

F. Instead of the return of the original check, the customer only has the right to _____

_____

G. To protect consumers from losses related to substitute checks, the Check 21 Act includes a consumer's right to claim _____

_____

_____

Legal Concepts

For each statement, write **T** *in the answer column if the statement is true or* **F** *if the statement is false.*
           Answer

1. The first bank to which an item is transferred for collection is the remitting bank.   **1.** _____

2. Collecting bank means any bank handling an item for collection except the payor bank.   **2.** _____

3. If the payor bank pays a check in cash, its payment is final.   **3.** _____

4. Any settlement given by a depository bank on a check is provisional.   **4.** _____

5. A debit card offers the same protection as a credit card.   **5.** _____

6. If a consumer notifies the issuer of the loss or theft of an ATM card within four business days, the consumer is liable for only $50 of any unauthorized withdrawals made with the card.   **6.** _____

7. The unautlorized use of an ATM card is a criminal offense.   **7.** _____

8. The drawee bank is under a duty to honor all checks drawn by its customers when there are sufficient funds on deposit.   **8.** _____

9. The Electronic Fund Transfer Act is a consumer protection law and does not apply to transactions between banks and other businesses.   **9.** _____

10. An antedated check is one that is delivered before its stated date.   **10.** _____

11. Banks must discontinue honoring checks of a deceased person within three days after the person's death.   **11.** _____

12. The bank is liable to a depositor if it gives payment for any check to which the depositor's signature has been forged.   **12.** _____

13. Banks must either pay or return checks on or before their midnight deadline.   **13.** _____

14. A banking day is any business day (up to the bank's cut-off hour) when the bank is open for substantially all of its banking activities.

14. _____

15. A written stop-payment order is binding for fourteen days.

15. _____

Language of the Law

Select the legal term that best matches each definition.

a. Check 21 Act
b. collecting bank
c. debit card
d. depository bank
e. electronic fund transfers
f. forgery
g. intermediary bank
h. midnight deadline
i. overdraft
j. payor bank
k. presenting bank
l. stale check
m. subrogation
n. substitute check
o. uttering

Answer

1. Any bank presenting an item except the payor bank

1. _____

2. A bank by which an item is payable as drawn or accepted

2. _____

3. A popular method of banking that uses computers and electronic technology as a substitute for checks and other banking methods

3. _____

4. A paper reproduction of both sides of an original check

4. _____

5. The situation that occurs when the bank pays out more money than the customer has on deposit

5. _____

6. The law that enables electronic check processing and cancels the right of customers to have their original canceled checks returned

6. _____

7. The act of fraudulently making or altering a check or other form of commercial paper to the injury of another

7. _____

8. A check card used to electronically subtract money from a bank account to pay for goods or services

8. _____

9. The offering of a forged instrument to another person, when the offeror knows the instrument has been forged

9. _____

10. A check that has been presented for payment more than six months after the date it was made out

10. _____

Applying the Law

1. Blair wrote a check on his New Hampshire bank for $948 to a Nevada company in payment for goods he had ordered from a catalog. Although it had been deducted from Blair's bank account, the Nevada company said that it did not receive it. Blair requested a copy of the canceled check from his bank and received a substitute check instead. Was Blair entitled to the return of the original canceled check? Explain.

_____

_____

_____

_____

2. Spencer was unaware that her debit card had been stolen from her pocketbook. Two weeks later when she learned that $860 had been withdrawn from her bank account without her knowledge, she notified the bank of the theft. Spencer felt relieved when a friend told her that she would only be responsible for paying $50 of the loss. Was the friend correct? Why or why not?

_____

_____

_____

_____

3. Szano wrote out several checks in payment of his monthly bills. He walked to the post office, mailed the checks, and, on the way home, was struck and killed by a speeding motorist. Since Szano was well-known in the community, the officers of the local bank knew of his death. Was the bank legally able to honor Szano's checks, which arrived a week after he died? Why or why not?

_____

_____

_____

_____

4. O'Connor, who had $6,000 in her bank account at Second State Bank, wrote a check to the order of Walsh Furniture Co., Inc., in the amount of $4,998. Walsh attempted to cash the check at the Second State Bank, but the bank refused to cash it under the mistaken belief that O'Connor had insufficient funds in the bank. Could Walsh sue the bank for refusing to honor the check? Explain.

_____

_____

_____

_____

5. Suppose that, in the above case, O'Connor had made the check out to Walsh Furniture Co. in payment for a set of furniture that was on sale for only three days, and the regular price of the furniture was $1,000 greater than the sale price. Suppose, also, that because of the failure of the bank to honor the check, Walsh Furniture Co. refused to sell the furniture to O'Connor at the sale price. Would the bank be responsible to O'Connor for the loss? Why or why not?

_____

_____

_____

_____

6. Amato, in reconciling her bank statement, discovered among her canceled checks a check that she had not written out. Upon careful examination it was found to be a clever forgery. Because Amato's genuine signature and the forged signature were very similar, the bank had not recognized the forgery. Was the bank liable to Amato for the amount of the forged check? Why or why not?

_____

_____

_____

_____

7. Richards gave his personal check in payment of his gas bill. The check was returned to the utility company by the bank marked "insufficient funds." Richards made no effort to pay the check when requested to do so by the payee. What crime, if any, did Richards commit?

_____

_____

_____

8. Horne went to his bank and deposited a $300 local check that was payable to him on Tuesday at 3:45 p.m. The bank's cut-off hour for the day's transactions was 2:00 p.m. Will the entire $300 be available to Horne on Thursday? Explain.

_____

_____

_____

9. Hernandez wrote out a check to Swift. Swift received the check, put it in her bureau drawer, and forgot about it. She came upon the check eight months later and attempted to cash it at the drawee bank. That bank refused to pay it, claiming that it could not do so by law because the check was so old. Was the bank correct? Why or why not?

_____

_____

_____

10. Popovic telephoned her bank requesting that it stop payment on a $97.50 check she had written that day in payment for a microwave oven that turned out to be defective. Three weeks later, the check was presented to the bank for the collection. The bank paid it and deducted $97.50 from Popovic's account. Did Popovic have legal recourse against the bank? Why or why not?

_____

_____

_____

Chapter 30   Insurance

Chapter Outline

30-1   **The Insurance Contract**

A. Risk management is used by many businesses to _____
_____
_____

B. Insurance is _____
_____

C. The parties to an insurance contract include _____
    1. _____
    2. _____
    3. _____

D. Insurance policies, like other contracts, require _____
_____
_____

E. Insurable interest is _____
_____

F. Insurance companies have the right to _____
_____
_____

30-2   **Types of Insurance**

A. Anyone has an insurable interest in the life of another if _____
_____

B. Straight life insurance requires _____
_____
_____

C. Straight life insurance contains two values:
    1. _____
    2. _____

D. Universal life insurance allows the policy owner _____
_____
_____

E. Limited-payment life insurance provides that_____
_____
_____

F. Term insurance is the least expensive kind of life insurance because
_____
_____

G. Endowment insurance combines _____

_____

H. An annuity is _____

_____

I. Many life insurance policies contain clauses that _____

_____

_____

J. Three popular optional provisions in life insurance policies are

1. _____

2. _____

3. _____

K. Property insurance can be made less expensive by _____

_____

L. The insurer and the insured share costs under _____

_____

M. A fire insurance policy is a contract in which _____

_____

N. Inland marine insurance covers _____

_____

O. Homeowner's insurance gives protection for _____

_____

P. Communities that do not participate in the National Flood
Insurance Program cannot _____

_____

Q. The most common types of automobile insurance are

1. _____   2. _____

3. _____   4. _____

5. _____   6. _____

7. _____   8. _____

9. _____   10. _____

R. People obtain health insurance through

1. _____

2. _____

3. _____

S. HMOs contract with doctors and other health are professionals to

_____

_____

T. The two parts of Medicare and their coverage are

1. _____

2. _____

U. Medicare is a healthcare plan for _____

_____

V. The two types of disability insurance are

1. _____

2. _____

W. National standards for all health plans are set by a federal law

known as _____

_____

30-3 **The Insurance**   **A.** A binder provides _____
Policy

_____

B. When the insured stops paying premiums, an insurance contract
is said to _____

_____

30-4 **Cancellation**   **A.** Conditions that permit the cancellation of an insurance policy
of Insurance   include
by Insurer

1. _____

2. _____

3. _____

B. Estoppel is _____

_____

_____

Legal Concepts

*For each statement, write **T** in the answer column if the statement is true or **F** if*   **Answer**
the statement is false.

1. The function of insurance is to distribute each person's risk among all
   others in a particular group, who may or may not experience loss.   **1.** _____

2. It is possible to obtain insurance against almost any risk if an individual
   or business is willing to pay the price.   **2.** _____

3. A life insurance policy becomes void if the insurable interest
   terminates.   **3.** _____

4. Property insurance will remain valid and enforceable even if the
   insurable interest terminates.   **4.** _____

5. In most cases, the courts allow a beneficiary to receive benefits under a
   life insurance policy if the insured is murdered.   **5.** _____

6. Beneficiaries are never allowed to recover the proceeds of an insurance
   policy if the insured commits suicide.   **6.** _____

7. Life insurance policies usually include an exemption from liability in times of war.

7. _____

8. Term insurance is the least expensive kind of life insurance because it has no cash or loan value.

8. _____

9. Fire insurance covers only those losses that result directly from fire.

9. _____

10. People who live in communities that do not participate in the National Flood Insurance Program cannot receive flood insurance for structures located in flood hazard areas of their community.

10. _____

11. No-fault insurance allows drivers to collect damages and medical expenses from the other driver's insurance carrier.

11. _____

12. Members of HMOs may choose any doctor of their choice.

12. _____

13. Automobile and property insurance policies usually have no grace periods and will terminate when a premium is not paid when due.

13. _____

14. In many states, by statute, the insurance company has the burden of proof in establishing that a warranty has been broken by the insured.

14. _____

15. To be legally effective, an insurance company's waiver of rights must always be in writing.

15. _____

Language of the Law

Select the legal term that best matches each definition.

a. Annuity
b. Beneficiary
c. collision insurance
d. comprehensive coverage
e. deductible

f. double indemnity
g. insurable interest
h. insurance
i. insured
j. insurer

k. Medicaid
l. medicare
m. premium
n. waiver
o. whole life insurance

1. An amount of a loss that is to be paid by the insured

1. _____

2. A third party who sometimes receives payment of compensation under an insurance contract

2. _____

3. The financial interest that a policyholder has in the person or property that is insured

3. _____

4. An accidental death benefit

4. _____

5. Automobile insurance that provides protection against loss due to fire, lightning, flood, hail, windstorm, riot, vandalism, and theft

5. _____

6. Consideration paid for insurance

6. _____

7. A transfer of risk of economic loss from the buyer to the seller, or to the insurance company

7. _____

8. The party protected by insurance

8. _____

9. Insurance that requires the payment of premiums throughout the life of the insured and pays the beneficiary the face value of the policy upon the insured's death

9. _____

10. A healthcare plan for low-income people funded by both state and federal funds

10. _____

Applying the Law

1. Immediately after Kathleen and Karl Fusco were married, they took out life insurance policies naming one another as beneficiaries. Their marriage ended in divorce after only one year. Nevertheless, they both continued to pay premiums on their policies and never changed the beneficiaries. When Kathleen died three years later, could Karl collect Kathleen's life insurance? Why or why not?

_____

_____

_____

2. Garvey sold a valuable Picasso original to Ovando. After the purchase, Ovando obtained insurance to cover damage to, or destruction of, the painting. Garvey's insurance policy covering the painting would not expire until six months after the sale. When the painting was destroyed by fire three weeks after the sale, who collected the insurance, Garvey or Ovando? Explain.

_____

_____

_____

3. Mayo took out a life insurance policy naming his wife as beneficiary. One year later, Mayo committed suicide. Will Mayo's wife receive the proceeds from the policy? Why or why not?

_____

_____

_____

4. Lisa and Anthony Darnell took out life insurance policies naming one another as beneficiaries. Each policy was for $100,000. When Lisa was killed in a boating accident, Anthony collected $200,000. Name and explain the optional provision that must have been included in their insurance policies.

_____

_____

_____

5. Jones purchased fire insurance to cover his winter home in Florida. During a tropical storm, Jones's winter home was struck by lightning, which severely damaged the front part of the house; however, no fire resulted. Jones's insurance agent told him that the damage was not covered under the fire insurance policy because no fire resulted. Was the agent correct? Why or why not?

_____

_____

_____

6. While driving on a vacation trip, Rosen lost control of his car. The car ran up on the curb, skidded over Kaplan's front lawn where it destroyed Kaplan's rose bushes, and then smashed into Kaplan's home. What type of auto insurance will Rosen need to cover him for all this property damage? if the insurance company refuses to pay and Kaplan brings suit, what will Kaplan have to prove to win the suit and receive payment for the damage to his property?

_____

_____

_____

7. Quin decided to take out an insurance policy to cover a collection of antique steam engines. On Monday he filled out an application with the National Insurance Company. Clifford, an agent for National, told Quin it would take until the following Monday for the main office to process the application. Quin was worried about the collection because of a rash of burglaries in his neighborhood. What should Quin and Clifford arrange while waiting for the main office to approve the policy?

_____

_____

_____

8. Watson applied for insurance with the Northern Insurance Company for coverage of his hunting lodge. When asked whether any explosives were stored on the property, Watson said there weren't. Actually, he had several sticks of dynamite in a storage chest on the back porch. The lodge was damaged in a windstorm, and the dynamite was discovered. Northern refused to pay Watson because of his lie. Will a court uphold this denial? Why or why not?

_____

_____

_____

9. Zanco, an insurance agent for the Allsafe Insurance Company, inspected Hyde's home prior to issuing an insurance policy. During the inspection, Zanco discovered that the home was located near a chemical dump. According to his company's specifications, the home was too close to the dump to be considered insurable, but Zanco issued the policy anyway. A month later, Hyde's home was damaged by a chemical fire originating in the dump. Did Allsafe have to pay for the damage? Why or why not?

_____

_____

_____

10. Schenk was a test pilot for Dagger Jet Air Production, Inc. After his third crash, Schenk was told by Ross, an insurance agent for Altar State Insurance, that his policy would be canceled unless he agreed to give up his work as a test pilot. Schenk agreed and a new policy was issued that included the new agreement. Schenk continued to fly and was killed in a crash one week later. Could Schenk's beneficiaries collect under the Altar State policy? Why or why not?

_____

_____

_____

Chapter 31   Mortgages and Security Devices

Chapter Outline

31-1 Necessity of Security Devices

A. A security device is _____
_____
_____

B. A secured loan is _____
_____
_____

C. A security interest is _____
_____
_____

D. An unsecured loan is _____
_____
_____

31-2 Real Property as Security

A. A mortgage is _____
_____
_____

B. An origination fee is_____
_____
_____

C. Points are _____
_____
_____

D. A conventional mortgage involves _____
_____
_____

E. A variable- or flexible-rate mortgage has a rate of interest that ____
_____
_____

F. A graduated-payment mortgage has a _____
_____
_____

G. A balloon-payment mortgage has _____
_____
_____

H. A reverse mortgage is _____

_____

_____

I. The FHA and VA are responsible to _____

_____

J. Under a deed of trust, the mortgagor conveys _____

_____

K. The Real Estate Settlement Procedures Act gives _____

_____

_____

L. Like a deed, a mortgage must be in writing and _____

_____

M. A junior mortgage is _____

_____

N. Home equity loans are often used to _____

_____

_____

O. The rights of the mortgagor include

   1. _____

   2. _____

   3. _____

P. The duties of the mortgagor include

   1. _____

   2. _____

Q. The mortgagee has the unrestricted right to _____

_____

31-3 Personal Property as Security

A. Collateral is _____

_____

_____

B. A security agreement is _____

_____

C. Attachment is _____

_____

D. A security interest can be perfected in three ways:

   1. _____

   2. _____

   3. _____

E. If a debtor defaults by failing to make payments when due, the secured party may satisfy the debt by _____

_____

_____

Legal Concepts

For each statement, write **T** *in the answer column if the statement is true or* **F** *if the statement is false.*　　　**Answer**

1. Debts are said to be secured when creditors are assured that somehow they will be able to recover their money.　　　1. _____

2. Most conventional mortgages involve an enormous amount of government backing.　　　2. _____

3. Variable mortgages need not include a maximum rate.　　　3. _____

4. The provisions of many deeds of trust allow a trustee to sell a property without going to court.　　　4. _____

5. A reverse mortgage allows homeowners over age 62 to convert some of the equity in their home to cash while retaining ownership of the home.　　　5. _____

6. A failure to record a first mortgage will erase the obligation of the first mortgagor to the first mortgagee.　　　6. _____

7. Under the PMI Act, homeowners must take out private mortgage insurance when they take out a mortgage with less than a 25% down payment.　　　7. _____

8. The mortgagee has the unrestricted right to sell, assign, or transfer the mortgage to a third party.　　　8. _____

9. Security agreements need not be in writing.　　　9. _____

10. Home equity loans, unlike credit card balances, are tax deductible.　　　10. _____

11. When a security interest attaches, it is effective between the debtor, the creditor, and all third parties.　　　11. _____

12. A perfected purchase money security interest in inventory has priority over a conflicting security interest in the same inventory.　　　12. _____

13. When a financing statement covers such products as crops, timber, minerals, oil, and gas, the statement must contain a description of the real estate associated with the product.　　　13. _____

14. When two or more parties have unperfected security interests in the same collateral, neither one prevail.　　　14. _____

15. After repossessing goods, the secured party may sell them at a public or private sale.　　　15. _____

Language of the Law

Select the legal term that best matches each definition.

a. acceleration
b. assume the mortgage
c. attachment
d. balloon-payment mortgage
e. deed of trust
f. foreclosure
g. graduated-payment mortgage
h. home equity loan
i. perfected
j. pledge
k. secured loan
l. secured party
m. security agreement
n. security interest
o. subject to the mortgage

Answer

1. A mortgage with monthly payments that increase over the term of the loan

   1. _____

2. The mortgagee's right to collect the entire balance due immediately upon the mortgagor's default on one installment payment

   2. _____

3. The right of a mortgagee to apply to a court to have property sold when the mortgagor defaults or fails to perform some agreement attached to the mortgage

   3. _____

4. An example of a junior mortgage

   4. _____

5. A mortgage with relatively low fixed-rate payments during the life of the mortgage followed by one large final payment

   5. _____

6. The right to use collateral to recover a debt

   6. _____

7. When a purchaser agrees to buy mortgage property and to make the mortgage payments

   7. _____

8. The legal enforceability of a security interest

   8. _____

9. A loan in which the creditor holds something of the debtor's that has value from which the creditor can be paid if the debtor defaults

   9. _____

10. A condition that exists when a secured party has done everything that the law requires to give the secured party greater rights to the goods than others have

    10. _____

Applying the Law

1. Ricci purchased a pizzeria for $150,000. He had only $20,000 in cash, so he took out a loan for $130,000 from the Fourth national Bank. When Ricci defaulted on the loan, the bank foreclosed and sold the store for $15,293 less than Ricci owed. Ricci believed he no longer owed the bank any money. Was Ricci correct? Explain.

_____
_____
_____
_____

2. Erik and Sonja Andrades purchased a home using a variable-rate mortgage. The rate of interest was tied to the bank's prime interest rate. At the time of the purchase, the rate was 8 percent. The agreement stated that the rate could change annually; however, no maximum rate was ever set. When the Andrades received notice that their interest rate would jump to 13 percent, they refused to pay the increase, arguing that the original agreement was unenforceable. Were they correct? Why or why not?

_____

_____

_____

3. Durbin purchased a home from Sealy using a deed of trust. The deed of trust was held by the Plymouth American Bank, which acted as trustee. When Durbin defaulted on the payments, the bank moved to sell the property without going through a court foreclosure process. Durbin argued that the bank must go to court before the property could be sold. Was he correct? Explain.

_____

_____

_____

4. Engel bought a summer cottage for $55,000. He financed it with a mortgage from Middlesex Building and Loan. Middlesex did not record the mortgage. Perry later bought the cottage from Engel. Perry conducted a search and found no mortgage recorded. Once the sale was completed, Engel argued that he no longer had any rights to the property, and, therefore, owed no money to Middlesex. Was he correct? Explain.

_____

_____

_____

5. Grasso financed the purchase of his beachfront property with a mortgage from the Medina County Farmers Bank. After making only one payment, he failed to make the next four. After repeated attempts to collect the installments plus late fees, Medina accelerated the debt, claiming that Grasso had to pay the full amount due or face foreclosure. Grasso argued that Medina had no right to accelerate the loan. Was Grasso correct? Explain.

_____

_____

_____

6. Mr. and Mrs. LaFrenz were both fifty-eight years old, were retired and needed some extra money. Since they owned their home free and clear, they decided to ask their bank for a reverse mortgage on the property. Will the bank grant them this type of loan? Why or why not?

_____

_____

_____

7. Sullivan, Inc., needed to purchase a fiberoptic splicer from Kellerson Electronics. Sullivan made a down payment on the splicer and signed a security agreement, agreeing that Kellerson could repossess the splicer if Sullivan defaulted on any future installment payments. Did Kellerson have a purchase money security interest in the equipment? Why or why not?

_____

_____

_____

8. Goodrich borrowed $1,000 from Vasquez. To secure the loan, Goodrich allowed Vasquez to take possession of his car. Since Vasquez had no garage, he made arrangements to rent space in his neighbor's garage to protect the car. When Goodrich paid off the debt and asked for the car, Vasquez demanded to be reimbursed for the money he'd spent to rent the garage space. Was Vasquez entitled to that reimbursement? Explain.

_____

_____

_____

9. Silvia and Avitto entered into an agreement whereby Avitto borrowed $10,000 from Silvia and Silvia took a security interest in Avitto's next corn and wheat harvest. The financing statement identified Silvia and Avitto by name and included their mailing addresses. Avitto signed the statement, which identified the corn and wheat crops. The county recorder rejected the financing statement. What element did Silvia and Avitto neglect to include?

_____

_____

_____

10. Russell borrowed $7,000 from the Lancaster Financial Network to purchase a motorcycle. Lancaster took a security interest in the cycle and perfected it by filing. Russell made no payments on the loan, so Lancaster sent Banner to repossess the cycle. When Banner arrived at Russell's house, Russell refused to let him near the cycle. Banner told Russell that he had the right to repossess the motorcycle for Lancaster even if he had to use force to do so. Was Banner correct? Explain.

_____

_____

_____

Chapter 32   Bankruptcy

Chapter Outline

32-1   Bankruptcy's History

A. Bankruptcy is _____
    _____
    _____
    _____

B. Under the first federal bankruptcy law in 1800, only creditors
    could _____ and only _____
    _____

C. In 1978 and 1994, bankruptcy reform acts made it easier for _____
    _____
    _____
    _____

D. The federal government receives jurisdiction over bankruptcy from
    _____
    _____

E. The Bankruptcy Code is found in_____
    _____
    _____

F. A personal bankruptcy filing remains on a debtor's credit report
    for _____

32-2   Liquidation - Chapter 7, Bankruptcy Code

A. Ordinary bankruptcy can begin in two ways
    1. _____
    2. _____

B. The means test consists of the following three steps:
    1. _____
    2. _____
    3. _____

C. If a single creditor is owed more than $ _____
    that creditor can file a(n) _____

D. An order for relief is_____
    _____
    _____

E. An automatic stay prohibits creditors from _____
    _____
    _____

F. Under the fresh-start approach, debtors can exclude the following from the bankruptcy process:

1. Homestead exemption $ _____
2. Total Household exemption $ _____
3. Jewelry $ _____
4. Professional tools, instruments and books $ _____
5. Motor vehicle $ _____

G. States may enact their own _____
_____

H. A debtor's debts are paid by a trustee in the following order:

1. _____ 2. _____
3. _____ 4. _____
5. _____ 6. _____
7. _____ 8. _____
9. _____ 10. _____

I. Exceptions to discharge in bankruptcy are:

1. _____
2. _____
3. _____

32-3 **Reorganization-Chapter 11, Bankruptcy Code**

A. Reorganization provides _____
_____
_____

B. Three qualities of a reorganization plan are:

1. _____
2. _____
3. _____

32-4 **Family Farmer or Fishing Business Debt Adjustment - Chapter 12, Bankruptcy Code**

A. The Family Farmer or Fishing Business Debt Adjustment Act is designed to _____
_____
_____

B. A Chapter 12 plan must include four provisions

1. _____
_____
2. _____
_____
3. _____
_____
4. _____
_____

32-5 **Individual Debt Adjustment - Chapter 13, Bankruptcy Code**

A. Chapter 13 of the Bankruptcy Code permits_____

_____

_____

B. Debts that cannot be discharged under Chapter 13 are

1. _____

2. _____

3. _____

Legal Concepts

For each statement, write **T** *in the answer column if the statement is true or* **F** *if the statement is false.*

Answer

1. Both the federal government and the states have jurisdiction over bankruptcy proceedings.

    1._____

2. Under Chapter 7 of the Bankruptcy Code, debtors are compelled to sell most of their property and use the cash to pay off their creditors.

    2._____

3. Voluntary bankruptcy filings are not allowed under Chapter 7.

    3._____

4. An automatic stay prohibits creditors from filing lawsuits against the debtor.

    4._____

5. Today, the number of business bankruptcy filings far exceeds the number of non-business bankruptcy filings.

    5._____

6. The Bankruptcy Code allows states to provide an alternate list of exemptions for debtors.

    6._____

7. Filing for bankruptcy does not allow a debtor to escape legal liability for any debt that arose from willful and malicious conduct.

    7._____

8. Debtors cannot discharge any cash advances that total more than $500 if those advances were obtained within twenty days of an order for relief.

    8._____

9. A Chapter 11 filing is not allowed for commodity brokers or stock brokers

    9._____

10. Under Chapter 11, a business must cease operation before a reorganization plan can go into effect.

    10._____

11. A Chapter 11 primary committee consists of the debtor's unsecured creditors.

    11._____

12. A Chapter 11 reorganization plan requires unanimous approval by all creditors.

    12._____

13. To qualify for a Chapter 12 filing, 80 percent of a farmer's debt must result from nonfarm expenses.

    13._____

14. Individuals, corporations, partnerships, and sole proprietorships can all file under Chapter 13.

    14._____

15. Under Chapter 13, the debtor must start payments within thirty days of submitting the plan to the court.

    15._____

Language of the Law

Select the legal term that best matches each definition.

a. automatic stay
b. bankruptcy
c. bankruptcy trustee
d. confirmation
e. debtor-in-possession

f. discharge
g. family farmer
h. homestead exemption
i. liquidation
j. mortgage

k. order for relief
l. primary committee
m. reorganization
n. unimpaired class
o. waiver

Answer

1. A court's command to begin a bankruptcy proceeding
1. _____

2. The individual charged with the responsibility of liquidating the assets of the debtor for the benefit of all interested parties
2. _____

3. Part of the value of the debtor's place of residence that is excluded from the bankruptcy process
3. _____

4. The legal process by which the assets of a debtor are sold to pay off creditors so that the debtor can make a fresh start financially
4. _____

5. A stay that stops the debtor's creditors from making further moves to collect the money that the debtor owes them
5. _____

6. Another name for ordinary bankruptcy
6. _____

7. A group of creditors who work with a debtor to set up a reorganization plan
7. _____

8. A group of creditors whose collection rights are not changed by a reorganization plan
8. _____

9. A debtor who continues to run a business after filing a Chapter 11 reorganization petition
9. _____

10. The official approval of a reorganization plan
10. _____

Applying the Law

1. Gomez owned a farm that had been badly undercapitalized from the start. After several years of operation, the financial condition of the farm was worse and several creditors decided to file an involuntary bankruptcy proceeding under Chapter 7. Gomez owed each of these creditors $2,500. Nevertheless, the involuntary petition was rejected. Why?

_____

_____

_____

_____

2. Loomis was so deeply in debt that she decided to file for bankruptcy under Chapter 7. An order for relief was issued, and the automatic stay went into effect. One of Loomis's creditors, the Flores Department Store, filed a lawsuit against Loomis in another court, believing the suit would be allowed because they'd filed it in a court other than the one handling the bankruptcy. Were they correct? Explain.

_____

_____

_____

3. Bavasi filed for bankruptcy under Chapter 7. Rogers was appointed as trustee. Could Rogers be assured that she would be paid for her services even though Bavasi was bankrupt? Explain.

_____

_____

_____

4. Mr. and Mrs. Wallace filed jointly for bankruptcy under Chapter 7. They decided to use their household exemption to protect a set of expensive furniture. Taken all together, the complete set was worth $15,000. At the time, the total of all exemptions taken in this category could not exceed $8,000. Was the furniture exempt from bankruptcy? Explain.

_____

_____

_____

5. Knowing that he would have to file for bankruptcy on the following Monday, Simmons used his bank card on Friday night to take out a $2,000 cash advance. He then spent the money on several expensive items, believing that he would never have to pay back the entire cash advance. Was Simmons correct in this assumption? Why or why not?

_____

_____

_____

6. Bennett and Cooper were partners in a family style restaurant that was having financial difficulties. The debts of the partnership were getting out of hand, and the partners knew they had to do something or they would lose the business. However, neither Bennett nor Cooper wanted to close down the business for good. Which chapter of the Bankruptcy Code should Bennett and Cooper file under? Why?

_____

_____

_____

7. Corrales purchased a computer from St. Clair Electronics for her small corporation. The computer was purchased on credit. Corrales had to make monthly payments of $125.50 on the computer debt. St. Clair retained a security interest in the computer with the right to repossess it should Corrales default. Corrales defaulted on three payments and filed for reorganization under Chapter 11. St. Clair argued that the electronics firm should be on the primary committee formed to work with Corrales. Was St. Clair correct? Why or why not?

_____

_____

_____

_____

8. Bowers owned a 50 percent interest in a farm in Nebraska. Approximately 25 percent of her income was derived from this farm. The rest of her income came from a variety of other investments, as well as her full-time job. When she lost her job and several of her investments failed, Bowers decided to file for debt adjustment as a farmer under Chapter 12. Was she able to do so? Why or why not?

_____

_____

_____

9. Baron and Nadel were partners in a hardware store. Due to several unwise purchases, they found themselves faced unsecured debts that they with $90,000 in unsecured debts that they could not cover. When they decided to file for debt adjustment under Chapter 13, they were told that chapter was not open to them. Why not?

_____

_____

_____

10. Grant had overextended himself financially and, as a result, had failed to pay several unsecured debts. After attempting to collect these debts in a number of different ways, three of Grant's creditors joined forces and filed a petition for an involuntary debt adjustment proceeding under Chapter 13. Their request was turned down. Why?

_____

_____

_____

_____

Chapter 33   The Principal and Agent Relationship

Chapter Outline

33-1   The Law of Agency

A. Agency is _____
_____

B. Principal-Agent Relationship
   1. An agent has authority to _____
   _____
   _____

   2. In an agency relationship, the principal is responsible for _____
   _____
   _____

C. Employer-Employee Relationship
   1. The main distinction between the agent-principal relationship
   and the employer-employee relationship is _____
   _____
   _____

   2. An employee who merely performs mechanical acts for the
   employer is _____
   _____
   _____

D. Master-Servant Relationship
   1. A master is _____
   _____

   2. A servant is _____
   _____

E. Proprietor-Independent Contractor Relationship
   1. An independent contractor is _____
   _____

   2. A proprietor has the right to _____
   _____
   _____

F. Why the Distinctions Are Important
   1. In contract law, unless an employee is also an agent _____
   _____
   _____

   2. In tort law, the doctrine of vicarious liability means _____
   _____

33-2 **Principles of Agency Law**

A. Types of Principals and Agents
  1. A disclosed principal is _____
     _____
  2. An undisclosed principal is _____
     _____
  3. A partially disclosed principal is _____
     _____
  4. A special agent is _____
     _____
  5. A general agent is _____
     _____
  6. A factor is _____
     _____

B. Liability of Principals and Agents
  1. The principal is liable on all _____
     _____
  2. An agent can be held liable when _____
     _____

C. Minors and Business Associations
  1. A principal who is not a minor may not _____
     _____
  2. A principal who is a minor may _____
     _____
     _____

33-3 **Creation of the Agency Relationship**

A. An agency is usually created by _____
   _____

B. Agency by necessity is created when _____
   _____

C. Agency by estoppel is created when _____
   _____

D. Agency by ratification occurs when _____
   _____

E. An electronic agent is _____
   _____

Legal Concepts

For each statement, write **T** *in the answer column if the statement is true or* **F** *if the statement is false.*

Answer

1. Agency relationships are always created as a result of a contract.
   1. _____
2. An agent has the authority to represent the principal.
   2. _____
3. All employees are agents.
   3. _____
4. A proprietor has the right to control the activities of a servant.
   4. _____
5. All independent contractors have the right to negotiate contracts.
   5. _____
6. Vicarious liability is based on the principle of *respondeat superior.*
   6. _____
7. When the master loans a servant to another master, the servant is referred to as a borrowed servant.
   7. _____
8. A nondelegable duty is one that cannot be passed off on another party.
   8. _____
9. No states have abolished sovereign immunity.
   9. _____
10. The Federal Torts Claim Act applies to state governments.
   10. _____
11. An employer is usually liable for the crimes of an employee.
   11. _____
12. A disclosed principal is known by a third party.
   12. _____
13. A principal may use the infancy of an agent to avoid liability under a contract.
   13. _____
14. The appointment of an agent by one partner is binding on all other partners.
   14. _____
15. Ratification has been outlawed in all states as a way of creating an agency.
   15. _____

Language of the Law

Select the legal term that best matches each definition.

a. agency
b. agent
c. borrowed servant
d. disclosed principal
e. general agent
f. master
g. nondelegable duty
h. negligent hiring
i. proprietor
j. special agent
k. vicarious liability

Answer

1. A person who is authorized to conduct a particular transaction
   1. _____
2. A principal whose identity is known to a third party
   2. _____
3. A legal agreement between two persons whereby one person is delegated the agent of the other
   3. _____
4. A person who has the right to control the activities of another person
   4. _____
5. A theory under which an employer may be held liable for the torts of the employee
   5. _____
6. A duty that cannot be passed of to another party
   6. _____

7. The failure to check an independent contractor's credentials before hiring might result in this

7. _____

8. A person who hires an independent contractor

8. _____

9. A person given broad authority to conduct the bulk of a principal's business

9. _____

10. A servant that has been loaned by one master to another

10. _____

Applying the Law

1. Clark was named to run the Clayborn General Store. He was given the power to hire and fire salespeople, buy and sell stock, supervise all operations, and make out the weekly work schedule. Name and explain the type of agent that Clark's authority made him.

_____

_____

_____

_____

2. Anderson was given the power to go to a real estate auction and make a bid on a house that had just been put up for sale. This was the only authority that Anderson had. Name and explain the type of agent that Anderson's authority made him.

_____

_____

_____

_____

3. McMahon hired a plumber to add a new bathroom to his basement. The plumber's only responsibility was to see that the bathroom was installed properly. McMahon could not direct the plumber's daily activities. What type of relationship existed between McMahon and the plumber? Explain.

_____

_____

_____

_____

4. Johnson worked as a delivery driver for Thomson Bakery. On a delivery run, he went through a stop sign and injured Gallery. Gallery sued not only Johnson but also the bakery. Explain why this was possible.

_____

_____

_____

_____

5. Nelson hired Frederick, a minor, to act as his agent in the purchase of an MP3 player. Later, Nelson attempted to get out of the contract by claiming that Frederick was a minor. Why did this tactic not work for Nelson? Explain.

_____

_____

_____

_____

6. Greggs, a famous basketball player, was in the market for a new house. Knowing that sellers would raise the prices of their homes if they knew he was the buyer, Greggs hired an agent to buy the house for him. Greggs told the agent that she could inform sellers that she was an agent but could not reveal his identity to potential sellers. Name and explain the type of principal Greggs had hired.

_____

_____

_____

_____

7. Selan, a famous rock star, was in the market for a new cabin cruiser. Knowing that sellers would raise the price of their cruisers if they knew she was the buyer, Selan hired an agent to buy the cabin cruiser for her. Selan told the agent that he should not even reveal that he is an agent. Name and explain the type of principal Selan had hired.

_____

_____

_____

_____

8. Mainland Airline hired the Terrance Maintenance Company, an independent contractor, to do repair work on all planes. Terrance made a serious error that caused the crash of one of Mainland's planes. One of the passengers sued Mainland. Mainland argued that it should not be held liable because Terrance was an independent contractor. Mainland was incorrect. Why?

_____

_____

_____

_____

9. Kramer Printing hired the Yesteryear Delivery Service, an independent contractor, to handle all its deliveries. Kramer did no checking to determine Yesteryear's record, which was very bad. Yesteryear drivers had been involved in seventeen accidents within the last three months. While on a delivery for Kramer, a Yesteryear driver had an accident injuring Usalis. Usalis wanted to sue Kramer despite the fact that Yesteryear was an independent contractor. What theory could Usalis use here? Why?

_____

_____

_____

_____

10. Macy purchased a painting for Harrison. Macy was not Harrison's agent. Nevertheless, Harrison liked the painting and continued to make payments under the terms negotiated by Macy. What legal process has occurred here? Why?

_____

_____

_____

_____

Chapter 34   Operation and Termination of Agency

Chapter Outline

34-1   Scope of an Agent's Authority

A. Express, Implied, and Apparent Authority
1. Express authority is_____
_____
2. Implied Authority is _____
_____
3. Apparent Authority is _____
_____

B. Should an agent delegate authority without authorization, then the acts of the subagent will be _____
_____

C. Nondelegable duties include _____
_____
_____

34-2   The Agent's Obligations to a Principal

A. Agents have the following obligations to their principals:
1. _____
_____
2. _____
_____
3. _____
_____
4. _____
_____
5. _____
_____
6. _____
_____

B. When an agent fails to observe a duty owed the principal, the principal has the following remedies available:
1. _____
_____
2. _____
_____
3. _____
_____

4. _____

5. _____

6. _____

7. _____

34-3 **The Principal's Obligations to the Agent**

A. The principal has the following obligations to the agent:

1. _____

2. _____

3. _____

4. _____

B. When a principal fails to observe a duty owed the agent, the agent has the following remedies available:

1. _____

2. _____

3. _____

4. _____

5. _____

34-4 **Termination of Agency**

A. An agency may be terminated by the acts of the parties in the following ways:

1. _____

2. _____

3. _____

B. An agency may be terminated by operation of law in the following
ways:

1. _____
   _____

2. _____
   _____

3. _____
   _____

4. _____
   _____

Legal Concepts

*For each statement, write **T** in the answer column if the statement is true or **F** if*   **Answer**
the statement is false.

1. Implied authority is the authority necessary to carry out the authorized
   duties of the agent.   1. _____
2. Express authority is the authority that the principal voluntarily and
   specifically sets forth as instructions in the agency agreement.   2. _____
3. Apparent authority involves something that the principal has done or said
   to lead a third party to the belief that agency authority does in fact exist.   3. _____
4. Reasonableness plays no role in the determination of the existence of
   apparent authority.   4. _____
5. An agent may not enter into an agency transaction in which the agent has
   a personal interest.   5. _____
6. Only agents who are paid for their agency activities are required to obey
   all reasonable and legal instructions issued by the principal.   6. _____
7. An agent may not engage in any activity that would result in a conflict of
   interest with the business of the principal.   7. _____
8. Money collected by the agent for the principal may be temporarily
   commingled with the agent's own funds.   8. _____
9. In the absence of the authority to do so, an agent may not delegate duties
   to others unless such duties require no particular knowledge, training, skill,
   or responsibility.   9. _____
10. The agent is bound by duty to keep the principal fully informed of all facts
    that may materially affect the subject matter of the agency.   10. _____
11. An agent may not recover compensation for illegal services unless they
    were rendered at the request of the principal.   11. _____
12. Agents cannot recover for expenses that arise from their own negligence.   12. _____
13. Agents are entitled to indemnification if they incur a loss or are damaged
    as a result of a principal's request.   13. _____

14. The insanity of the principal, but not of the agent, will usually terminate the authority of the agent.   14. _____

15. The principal is never required to notify third parties of the agency's termination.   15. _____

Language of the Law

Select the legal term that best matches each definition.

a. agency coupled with an Interest
b. apparent authority
c. durable power of attorney
d. express authority

e. implied authority
f. indemnification
g. lingering apparent authority
h. renunciation

i. revocation
j. scope of authority
k. Uniform Durable Power of Attorney Act

		Answer
1.	Authority needed to carry out the authorized duties of the agent	1. _____
2.	Authority voluntarily and specifically set forth by the principal	2. _____
3.	Payment to the agent for loss or damage suffered in carrying out the principal's business	3. _____
4.	Authority created by something that the principal says or does in relation to a third party	4. _____
5.	Authority that remains when the principal does not notify a third party that the agent has been discharged	5. _____
6.	A termination of an agency that occurs when the principal takes back the agent's authority	6. _____
7.	A termination of an agency that occurs when an agent voluntarily gives up the power granted by the principal	7. _____
8.	The range of acts authorized by the principal	8. _____
9.	An agency agreement in which the agent is given an interest in the subject matter of the agency	9. _____
10.	The preservation of the power of an agent should the principal become incapacitated	10. _____

Applying the Law

1. Henry was hired by Palla to be a sales clerk in Palla's SciFi Bookstore. Palla instructed Henry to sell on a cash basis only. When Denmark, a regular customer, asked Henry for credit in the purchase of an encyclopedia, Henry agreed. When Palla discovered this he fired Henry. Was Palla within his rights in discharging Henry? Explain.

_____

_____

_____

_____

2. Allen was hired to work as a purchasing agent for Kerry's computer store. Using his own money, Allen purchased several computers from a manufacturer. He then resold the computers to Kerry at an enormous profit. Name and explain the duty that Allen violated here.

_____

_____

_____

_____

3. McClain worked as a delivery person for the Razor Cola Company. In this capacity, he recently collected money from customers for Razor. One week he carelessly let his son deposit the money. His son deposited the money in McClain's personal account. When McClain tried to retrieve the money he did not know how much belonged to Razor. What legal remedy does Razor have against McClain? Explain.

_____

_____

_____

_____

4. Hurley, a certified public accountant, was hired by Olley to figure out Olley's taxes. Hurley hired a recent high school graduate to do Olley's taxes. May Olley refuse to honor this appointment? Explain

_____

_____

_____

_____

5. Benrit was a purchasing agent for Mueller Appliances. Finley, a salesperson for Sandusky Furniture, told Benrit that the furniture that he wanted had doubled in price. Benrit went ahead and purchased the furniture anyway. When Mueller found out about the price increase, he refused to honor the contract. Can Sandusky sue Mueller for breach of contract? Explain.

_____

_____

_____

_____

6. While on a business trip to Atlanta for Gunderson Inc., Bailey attended the first game of the World Series. When Bailey sought reimbursement, Gunderson refused to honor the request. Was Gunderson acting correctly? Explain.

_____

_____

_____

_____

7. Thomson worked as a purchasing agent for United Enterprises. Because of certain company policies, he was required to use his own money in some purchases. Must United Enterprises repay these out-of-pocket expenses? Explain.

_____

_____

_____

_____

8. Wilson hired Eddenson to sell Wilson's helicopter. Before any sale could be made, the helicopter was destroyed by a crash. The destruction of the helicopter terminated the agency by operation of law. Whom must Wilson inform of the termination? Explain.

_____

_____

_____

_____

9. Olsen worked as a door-to-door sales person for January Cosmetics. As a part of his activity, he frequently collected money from customers for January. Would Olsen be allowed to deposit funds in his own account until January asks him to deliver the money? Explain.

_____

_____

_____

_____

10. Pearsal hired Huxley to be a sales clerk in Pearsal's Personal Gift Shop. Pearsal told Huxley never to take a check from Jameson. When Jameson tried to purchase an antique clock, Huxley took Jameson's check. When Pearsal discovered this, he fired Huxley. Was Pearsal within his rights in firing Huxley? Explain.

_____
_____
_____
_____

Chapter 35   Employment Law

Chapter Outline

35-1 Laws Employment Relationship

A. The doctrine of employment-at-will means_____

_____

_____

B. A collective bargaining agreement is_____

_____

_____

C. People who can negotiate their own individual professional employment contracts include _____

_____

D. Under the Worker Adjustment and Retraining Notification Act, there are some employers who must _____

_____

E. The protected classes set up by Congress in the Civil Rights Act of 1964 include the following _____

_____

F. Several theories have been developed by state courts to limit employment-at-will. They include

   1. _____

_____

   2. _____

_____

   3. _____

_____

   4. _____

_____

   5. _____

_____

G. The after acquired evidence defense is used when _____

_____

35-2 Laws Regulating Employment Conditions

A. The Occupational Safety and Health Administration establishes

_____

_____

B. The Fair Labor Standards Act provides_____

_____

C. The Immigration Reform Act of 1986 created _____

_____

_____

35-3 Worker Benefits

A. The Social Security Act of 1935 is the primary federal law covering

_____

B. The unemployment insurance section of the Social Security Act provides for _____

_____

C. State workers' compensation laws compensate workers or their dependents for _____

_____

D. The federal Employee Retirement Income Security Act of 1974 (ERISA) provides _____

_____

_____

E. The federal Family and Medical Leave Act (FMLA) requires employers to _____

_____

_____

35-4 Equal Employment Opportunity

A. The Equal Pay Acts states that employers must _____

_____

B. The Civil Rights Act of 1964 prohibits _____

C. The Civil Rights Act of 1991 meets the following objectives:

1. _____

2. _____

D. The Age Discrimination in Employment Act prohibits _____

_____

E. The Uniformed Services Employment and Reemployment Rights Act guarantees that _____

_____

F. The Americans with Disabilities Act is designed to _____

_____

_____

Legal Concepts

For each statement, write **T** *in the answer column if the statement is true*
or **F** *if the statement is false.*

Answer

1. The after acquired evidence defense is sometimes available for employers who have discovered evidence that would have allowed them to discharge an employee even if the wrongful discharge claim was true.

1. _____

2. Promissory estoppel does not involve an element of reasonableness.

2. _____

3. There are no exceptions to the requirements laid down by WARN.

3. _____

4. Wrongful discharge is sometimes referred to as unjust dismissal.

4. _____

5. Intentional infliction of emotional distress may be considered as the basis for wrongful discharge when the employer's conduct is extreme and outrageous.

5. _____

6. The after acquired evidence defense has never been used in discrimination lawsuits.

6. _____

7. To be effective, a disclaimer must be written in clear, unequivocal language.

7. _____

8. To be effective, a disclaimer must be placed somewhere conspicuous.

8. _____

9. Only written contracts can create employment relationships.

9. _____

10. Under a grievance procedure, employees have the right to appeal an employer's decision that they believe is unjust.

10. _____

11. The only type of discrimination is disparate treatment.

11. _____

12. OSHA establishes federal health and safety standards for the workplace.

12. _____

13. Implied contract is the only grounds recognized by the courts for wrongful discharge cases.

13. _____

14. WARN establishes federal requirements for employee leave situations involving child, spousal, or parental care situations.

14. _____

15. The Americans with Disabilities Act (ADA) does not define disability.

15. _____

Language of the Law

Select the legal term that best matches each definition.

a. affirmative action
b. disability
c. disclaimer
d. disparate impact

e. disparate treatment
f. employment-at-will
g. grievance procedure
h. implied contract

i. *quid pro quo* sexual harassment
j. worker's compensation
k. wrongful discharge

1. Sexual harassment that suggests trading sexual favors for some sort of employment advantage

2. A wrongful discharge theory that applies when an employer has said or done something that leads an at-will employee to believe that he or she has an employment contract

3. Indirect discrimination

4. A clause in an employment manual designed to preserve employment-at-will

5. Deliberate discrimination

6. A legal theory that gives employees who have been dismissed unfairly legal grounds for a lawsuit

7. The legal theory that says that an employer can dismiss an employee at any time for any reason

8. Any physical or mental impairment that substantially limits one or more of the major life functions

9. A procedure that gives employees the right to appeal an employer's decision

10. A system that compensates workers or their dependents for injuries, disease, or death that occurs on the job or as a result of the job

Answer

1. _____
2. _____
3. _____
4. _____
5. _____
6. _____
7. _____
8. _____
9. _____
10. _____

Applying the Law

1. Jack Garfield worked as a bank teller for he Farmers' Savings and Loan. Although he was a loyal and competent worker, he was discharged so that the head of the S&L could give the job to someone else. Garfield was an at-will employee. Under the doctrine of employment-at-will, what were Garfield's legal rights?

_____

_____

_____

_____

2. Eduardo Samuels worked as an electrician for The Delaware Electrical Supply Corporation. He was also a member of the United Electrical Workers of America (UEWA). Samuels was discharged when he reported for work late. The collective bargaining agreement between Delaware and the UEWA forbade the discharge of an employee for a single incidence of lateness. Any violations were to be in writing and workers were to be given a second chance. What recourse did Samuels have? Explain.

_____

_____

_____

_____

3. Briana Morley, who worked for the Heisenberg Research Corporation, took a leave of absence for health reasons. Her supervisor, Gary Planck, told Morley, "When your medical problem is cured, you can have your job back with full seniority." Morley believed Planck and did not look for employment elsewhere. When she returned to work, Morley found that Heisenberg would not honor Planck's promise. It took Morley six months to find a job. Did Morley have any legal recourse? Explain.

_____

_____

_____

4. Casey Hawkins applied for a job as a physicist with the VonBraun Research Corporation. The employee handbook included a disclaimer that said that employees could be discharged with or without notice at any time for any reason and even without a reason. Only the president of VonBraun could alter this provision. Hawkins, who had other job prospects lined up, told Werner Goddart, who wanted to hire Hawkins, that she would not work under such a provision. Goddart told her to ignore the disclaimer and promised Hawkins a job for life. Was Goddart's promise legally effective? Explain.

_____

_____

_____

_____

5. Jim Hubble was to receive a 10 percent commission on all sales he made for his employer, the Radical Computer Corporation. Hubble sold a $10 million computer system to NASA for a new orbiting laboratory. To avoid paying $1 million to Hubble, Radical fired him, despite his record as an excellent salesperson. Hubble's state recognizes the implied covenant theory of wrongful discharge. Explain the legal rights that this theory would give to Hubble.

_____

_____

_____

6. Luisa Hegel, a respiratory therapist, was laid off from her job with the Akron City Center Hospital because of economic conditions. She registered with the state unemployment compensation agency and requested unemployment compensation. The interviewing official told her about a job opening for a respiratory therapist at the Canton Clinic. Hegel refused it on the grounds that she needed a vacation before accepting another job. Would Hegel qualify for unemployment compensation? Explain.

_____

_____

_____

_____

7. The *Fashion Leader,* a magazine that featured women's fashions, advertised for female models for a special swimwear issue. Explain why such a hiring practice would not violate the Civil Rights Act of 1964.

_____

_____

_____

_____

8. Yulanda Uttermeyer, age sixty-two, lost her position when the subsidiary she worked for was disbanded by the Hume Petrochemical Corporation, the parent corporation. All of the employees who were laid off as a result of the closing were promised preferential treatment for other jobs at Hume. Uttermeyer applied for over fifty of these positions. She was never rehired. The reason given for her rejection was that she was overqualified. Uttermeyer believed that she could bring an age discrimination suit under the ADEA. Was she correct? Explain.

_____

_____

_____

_____

9. Gerhart brought a discrimination case against the Portland Area School Board under Title VII of the Civil Rights Act of 1964 as amended in 1991. Gerhart claimed that she had been discriminated against because of her religious beliefs. Gerhart has asked for compensatory and punitive damages. The Portland Area School Board has argued that only victims of racial discrimination can collect compensatory and punitive damages under the Civil Rights Act. Is the board correct? Explain.

_____

_____

_____

_____

10. Georgette MacKay has a visual disability. She applied for a position as an accountant with the Daystrom Corporation. Frederick Hansen, the human resources director, tested her eyesight by having her read several documents in very fine print. MacKay failed the test and, on that basis alone, was rejected. MacKay believed that Daystrom violated the ADA. Was she correct? Explain.

_____

_____

_____

_____

Chapter 36   Labor-Management Relations Law

Chapter Outline

36-1 Labor Law and the Complex Adaptive System

A. A Complex Adaptive Tug-of-War
  1. The Sherman Antitrust Act was used by big business and the courts to_____
  _____
  _____
  _____

  2. One of the objectives of the Clayton Act was to _____
  _____
  _____

  3. The two tests used by the courts to circumvent the Clayton Act were
    a._____
    _____
    b._____
    _____

  4. The net effect of the Norris-LaGuardia Act was _____
  _____
  _____
  _____

B. The three objectives of a labor union are
  1. _____
  2. _____
  3. _____

36-2 Major Federal Labor Legislation

A. The activities outlawed by the Wagner Act include
  1. _____
  2. _____
  3. _____
  4. _____
  5. _____

B. The Taft-Hartley Act established _____
  _____
  _____

C. The Landrum-Griffin Act is designed to _____
  _____
  _____

36-3	**The Collective Bargaining Process**	**A.** The National Labor Relations Board

A. The National Labor Relations Board

   1. The NLRB is _____

_____

_____

   2. The NLRB has the power to _____

_____

_____

B. Unfair Labor Practice Procedure

   1. Arbitration involves _____

_____

_____

   2. If an NLRB complaint is found to be valid _____

_____

_____

C. The Right to Strike in the Public Sector

   1. Strikes by public employees are generally _____

_____

_____

   2. The Supreme Court has affirmed _____

_____

_____

Legal Concepts

For each statement, write **T** *in the answer column if the statement is true or* **F** *if the statement is false.*   **Answer**

1. Union organizing activities are protected by federal and state laws, as well as by the U.S. Constitution.   **1.** _____

2. The first federal statute relating to labor was the Taft-Hartley Act.   **2.** _____

3. The Railway Labor Act does not deal with the airline industry.   **3.** _____

4. The Norris-LaGuardia Act gave the federal courts the power to grant injunctions prohibiting striking, picketing, and boycotting.   **4.** _____

5. The Wagner Act gave workers the right to organize, join, and aid labor unions.   **5.** _____

6. The Taft-Hartley Act created the NLRB.   **6.** _____

7. Under the Wagner Act, employers are permitted to reward workers who do not participate in union activities.   **7.** _____

8. The Taft-Hartley Act includes a free speech provision that allows employers to comment more freely on union organizing activities.   **8.** _____

9. Under the Wagner Act, employers are permitted to form company-run unions as long as they follow the union certification procedures.   **9.** _____

10. The Wagner Act permits closed shop agreements between the employer and the union.   **10.** _____

11. Unions can set rules for their internal operation and can punish union members who disobey those rules.   11. _____

12. The Taft-Hartley Act permits only secondary boycotts.   12. _____

13. The Landrum-Griffin Act established a "bill of rights" to allow employees to participate in certain selected union procedures.   13. _____

14. Decisions by the NLRB may be appealed to the appropriate U.S. Court of Appeals and then to the Supreme Court.   14. _____

15. In the public sector, strikes by employees performing vital services are generally illegal unless specifically authorized by statute.   15. _____

Language of the Law

Select the legal term that best matches each definition.

a. arbitration	**e.** featherbedding	**i.** secondary boycott
b. bargaining unit	**f.** hot-cargo contract	**j.** strike
c. closed shop	**g.** labor union	**k.** unfair labor practices
d. constructive discharge	**h.** right-to-work laws	**l.** union shop

Answer

1. Keeping unneeded employees, paying employees for not working, or assigning more employees than needed to a given job   1. _____

2. A place of employment where nonunion workers may be employed for a trial period of not more than thirty days after which nonunion workers must join the union or be discharged   2. _____

3. An improper employment practice by either an employer or a union   3. _____

4. A work stoppage by employees as a way to enforce demands made on the employer   4. _____

5. An organization of employees that acts on behalf of all employees of a particular group in negotiations with the employer regarding terms of their employment   5. _____

6. A worksite in which the employer, by agreement, hires only union members   6. _____

7. The submission of a dispute to selected persons and the substitution of their decision for the judgment of the NLRB   7. _____

8. Assigning an employee to undesirable work in retaliation for union activities   8. _____

9. State laws that prohibit labor-management agreements requiring union membership as a condition of employment   9. _____

10. A unit formed for the purpose of collective bargaining   10. _____

Applying the Law

1. Wiley owned and operated the Wiley Fireworks Corporation, a novelty shop with six stores. Wiley discovered that one of his employees planned to hold a meeting in order to discuss the possibility of forming a union. Wiley placed a notice on the bulletin board in each store warning employees that any employee who joined a union would be subject to immediate dismissal. Did such a notice violate federal law? Explain.

_____

_____

_____

_____

2. Hanson owned and operated a chain of sporting goods stores in several states, including Vermont, New Hampshire, and Massachusetts. When Hanson found out that his employees had decided to form a union, he sent out a letter that said that any employee who refused to join a union would receive an extra week's paid vacation. Did such a letter violate federal law? Explain.

_____

_____

_____

_____

3. The entire teaching staff of Sts. Peter and Paul University met with the Archbishop of Detroit and informed him that they intended to form a union. They demanded a collective bargaining agreement from the archbishop, who refused. The teachers told the archbishop that they planned to take their case to the NLRB. Can the teachers do this? Explain.

_____

_____

_____

4. Ackerman owned and operated a chain of reducing salons throughout the Pacific Northwest. When she found out that Dillard, one of her employees, had plans to form a union, she transferred him from Seattle and demoted him from store manager to sales clerk. The move meant a pay cut and a loss of seniority for Dillard. What illegal employment practice did Ackerman use here? Explain.

_____

_____

_____

_____

5. Chesterland ran a chain of bookstores in Virginia, Maryland, and West Virginia. When she learned that one of her employees intended to form a union, she put together a company run union to prevent the organization of the other union. She later found out that such a tactic was illegal. Explain.

_____

_____

_____

_____

6. Langhorne was president of the Montana and Idaho Book Binding Company. Edwards, an employee of Montana and Idaho, told Langhorne that the employees wanted to form a union. Upon learning of this plan, Langhorne called a meeting to explain his point of view on the effects of unionizing. Edwards told Langhorne that such a meeting was illegal. Was Edwards correct? Explain.

_____

_____

_____

_____

7. Union representatives and corporate officers of the Fairfax Tire Company met in a collective bargaining session to negotiate a new contract. As part of the new contract, the union representatives demanded that twelve people be added to each shift even though they knew only eight people were needed. Corporate officials, confident of their position, correctly refused to comply with the request. Why?

_____

_____

_____

_____

8. Mulligan, a new member of the Federated International Workers Union, asked to speak at the next union meeting. Gleason, president of the union, told Mulligan that he would have to be a union member for five years before he would be allowed to speak at union meetings. Was Gleason correct? Explain

_____

_____

_____

_____

9. Catlin owned and operated the Hapwood Corporation, which had stores in West Virginia, Pennsylvania, and Kentucky. When he found out that union members were forcing workers to join the union, he threatened to file a notice with the NLRB. Keene, a union official, argued that only union members could file notice with the NLRB. Was Keene correct? Explain.

_____

_____

_____

_____

10. Employees of the U.S. Defense Department, unhappy over low wages, decided to strike. When a federal court ordered the strikers back to work, they refused to obey, citing their constitutional right to strike. The strikers were fired, and the union was fined. Explain this result.

_____

_____

_____

_____

Chapter 37   Sole Proprietorships and Partnerships

Chapter Outline

37-1   Sole Proprietorship

A. A sole proprietorship is _____
_____
_____
_____

B. Advantages and Disadvantages of a Sole Proprietorship
    1. The greatest advantage of a sole proprietorship is _____
_____
_____

    2. The major disadvantage of a sole proprietorship is _____
_____
_____

37-2   General Partnership Characteristics

A. The Revised Uniform Partnership Act is _____
_____
_____
_____

B. A partnership is _____
_____
_____
_____

C. The Entity and Aggregate Theories
    1. Under the entity theory a partnership exists as_____
_____
_____

    2. Under the aggregate theory a partnership is seen as_____
_____
_____

37-3   Partnership Formation

A. A partnership agreement is _____
_____
_____

B. Partnership by Proof of Existence has three elements:
    1. _____
    2. _____
    3. _____

37-4 Partnership Property Rights and Duties

A. The RUPA defines partnership property as _____

_____

_____

B. The RUPA change the rules regarding specific partnership property when its stated _____

_____

_____

C. An interest in the partnership firm has two parts:

  1. _____

  2. _____

D. The five rights that partners have are:

  1. _____

  2. _____

  3. _____

  4. _____

  5. _____

37-5 Dissociation and Dissolution

A. Dissociation is _____

_____

_____

B. Dissolution is _____

_____

_____

A. A registered limited liability partnership is _____

_____

_____

B. A limited partnership is _____

_____

_____

Legal Concepts

For each statement, write **T** *in the answer column if the statement is true or* **F** *if the statement is false.*   **Answer**

1. Sole proprietorships are very difficult to start up.   **1.** _____

2. Sole proprietors may sometimes have to check zoning restrictions, licensing laws, and filing requirements.   **2.** _____

3. A major disadvantage of a sole proprietorship is unlimited liability.   **3.** _____

4. Sole proprietors sometimes find it difficult to raise a lot of cash for their businesses.   **4.** _____

5. The existence of a sole proprietorship does not depend upon the existence of the sole proprietor.   5. _____

6. Partnerships must involve at least three people.   6. _____

7. The sharing of profits is considered to be *prima facie* evidence for the existence of a partnership.   7. _____

8. Partnership agreements can never be oral.   8. _____

9. A person is not a partner if his or her share of the profits is a rental payment.   9. _____

10. Partnership by estoppel creates a true partnership.   10. _____

11. A partner's tenancy in partnership rights may never be assigned to a nonpartner unless the other partners consent.   11. _____

12. A partner's share of the profits may never be assigned to a nonpartner unless the other partners consent.   12. _____

13. Under provisions of the Revised Uniform Partnership Act a partnership is to be considered an aggregate of the partners.   13. _____

14. Limited Liability Partnerships eliminate contract liability.   14. _____

15. The formation of an LLP does not require the filing of a registration statement.   15. _____

Language of the Law

Select the legal term that best matches each definition.

a. aggregate theory
b. capital contribution
c. dissociation
d. dissolution
e. entity theory
f. limited liability
g. limited partnership
h. partnership
i. secret partner
j. silent partner
k. sole proprietorship
l. term partnership

		Answer
1.	A business run by a single individual	1. _____
2.	An association of two or more persons to carry on a business for profit	2. _____
3.	A partnership formed by two or more persons having at least one general and one limited partner	3. _____
4.	A legal theory that says that a partnership exists as an individual person having its own identity	4. _____
5.	A partner who does not participate in the day-to-day business of the firm	5. _____
6.	A partnership set up to run for a certain period of time	6. _____
7.	The event that occurs when one partner ceases to be associated with running of the partnership	7. _____
8.	A legal theory that holds that a partnership is an assembly of the partners	8. _____
9.	A partner whose identity and existence are not known outside of the firm	9. _____
10.	Sums contributed by partners as permanent investments	10. _____

Applying the Law

1. Cooke and Corbin formed a partnership to sell tires for trucks and automobiles. They leased a warehouse from Strong and paid him rent of $1,000 per month. When the partnership dissolved, Strong claimed he was a partner because he'd shared in Cooke's and Corbin's profits. Was Strong wrong? Explain.

_____

_____

_____

_____

2. Foster and Banner were partners in a printing business. They purchased several hundred gallons of ink from the Silvermine Ink Corporation. When they had difficulty paying their bills, an attorney for Silvermine told Foster that the corporation was going to try to force him to sell his car to pay for the ink. Silvermine was unable to do this. Why?

_____

_____

_____

_____

3. Rooney and Jinn entered into an oral partnership agreement. Rooney later backed out of the agreement, claiming that it was unenforceable. Was he correct? Explain.

_____

_____

_____

_____

4. Harrigan and Fenn were partners in a music store. Harrigan owed Galt $1,500 on a personal debt. Galt had threatened to go to court to force the partnership to sell its computer to satisfy Harrigan's personal debt to him. Would Galt be able to do this? Explain.

_____

_____

_____

_____

5. Hawkens, Cohen, and Newton were partners in a drugstore. Hawkens decided to assign his share of the profits to his daughter. Cohen and Newton claimed that this action would dissolve the partnership. Were they correct? Explain.

_____

_____

_____

_____

6. Robinson, Lopez, and Curren were partners in a bookstore. Robinson felt that they should purchase a computer for the store. Lopez and Curren disagreed. Robinson purchased the computer anyway. He then asked Lopez and Curren to reimburse him for the money he spent on the computer system, which they refused to do. Was their refusal legally correct? Explain.

_____

_____

_____

_____

7. Ricardo, Orwell, and Pembroke voted to make Radford a new partner in their firm. Simpson, a fourth partner, objected to the admission of Radford. Ricardo, Orwell, and Pembroke argued that Simpson's lone dissenting vote did not matter because they had a majority on their side. Were they correct? Explain.

_____

_____

_____

_____

8. Wong and Blum were partners in a clothing store. While on a routine delivery, Blum caused an accident when he ran a stoplight. Wong claimed that only Blum would be liable for the injuries sustained by the other driver. Was Wong correct? Explain.

_____

_____

_____

_____

9. As partners, O'Connor and Welsh ran a drycleaning business. After five years, it became clear that the business could be carried on only at a loss. O'Connor wanted to shut down operations. Welsh did not. O'Connor argued that since the partnership could be operated only at a loss, it was dissolved by operation of law. Was O'Connor correct? Explain.

_____

_____

_____

_____

10. Fletcher was the limited partner and Harkins the general partner in the Green Lawn and Supply Emporium. Schaps knew Fletcher was supposed to be a limited partner. However, when Schaps filed suit against Green to recover a debt, he named Fletcher as a party to the suit because Schaps had found out that a certificate of limited partnership had not been filed. Nevertheless, Schap's addition of Fletcher to the suit was incorrect. Why?

_____

_____

_____

_____

Chapter 38   The Corporate Entity

Chapter Outline

38-1   The Corporation in the Complex Adaptive System

A. Associative corporativism is _____
_____
_____

B. Limited liability is _____
_____

C. As a legal entity, a corporation can _____
_____

D. Within the 14th Amendment, a corporation may not _____
_____
_____

E. A corporation is a citizen of _____
_____

38-2   Types of Corporate Entities

A. Private, Public, and Quasi-Public
  1. A private corporation is _____
  _____

  2. A public corporation is _____
  _____

  3. A quasi-public corporation is_____
  _____

B. Domestic, Foreign, and Alien
  1. A domestic corporation is _____
  _____

  2. A foreign corporation is_____
  _____

  3. An alien corporation is_____
  _____

C. Close and S Corporations
  1. A close corporation is _____
  _____

  2. An S corporation is _____
  _____

D. A limited liability company is _____
_____
_____

38-3 Corporate Formation

A. Promoters are _____

_____

The Articles of Incorporation are _____

_____

B. A corporate name must include _____

_____

C. The articles are approved by _____

_____

D. Bylaws are _____

_____

E. The articles of organization of a LLC are _____

_____

38-4 Defective Incorporation

A. A *de jure* corporation is _____

_____

B. A *de facto* corporation is _____

_____

_____

C. Corporation by estoppel is _____

_____

_____

38-5 Piercing the Corporate Veil

A. Veil piercing involves _____

_____

_____

B. A dummy corporation is _____

_____

_____

38-6 Corporate Finance

A. A stock certificate is _____

_____

_____

B. Dividends
  1. Common stock is _____

_____

  2. Preferred stock is _____

_____

  3. Par value is _____

_____

Legal Concepts

For each statement, write **T** *in the answer column if the statement is true or* **F** *if the statement is false.*

Answer

1. A limited liability company requires five persons to incorporate.

   1. _____

2. A limited liability company is best thought of as a cross between a partnership and a corporation.

   2. _____

3. The people who run limited liability companies are called managers.

   3. _____

4. The members of a limited liability company do not have to create an operating agreement.

   4. _____

5. The members of a limited liability company do not have to file articles of organization.

   5. _____

6. All states require written modifications to an LLC's operating agreement.

   6. _____

7. The tax status of an LLC depends upon an election made by the owners of the LLC.

   7. _____

8. As a legal entity, a corporation can own property but can neither sue or be sued.

   8. _____

9. A corporation is considered a citizen of only the state in which it is incorporated.

   9. _____

10. Promoters have a fiduciary relationship with the not-yet-existent corporation and its future shareholders.

    10. _____

11. Piercing the corporate veil applies only to large corporations.

    11. _____

12. Corporation by estoppel creates a real corporation.

    12. _____

13. Holders of common stock are guaranteed to receive dividends quarterly.

    13. _____

14. All states have authorized corporations to issue stock with no par value.

    14. _____

15. The most common kind of dividend is the cash dividend.

    15. _____

Language of the Law

Select the legal term that best matches each definition.

a. alien corporation
b. articles of organization
c. certificate of authority
d. certificate of incorporation
e. close corporation
f. corporate shell
g. common stock
h. corporation
i. corporation by estoppel
j. *de facto* corporation
k. *de jure* corporation
l. dividends
m. limited liability corporation
n. operating agreement

Answer

1. Written application to the state for permission to form a limited liability company

   1. _____

2. A document that is helpful in establishing the bylaws of a limited liability company

   2. _____

3. A document that grants a foreign corporation permission to do business in another state
3. _____

4. A corporation's official authorization to do business in the state of incorporation
4. _____

5. Net profits or surplus set aside for the shareholders of a corporation
5. _____

6. A corporation whose existence is the result of the incorporators having complied with the relevant incorporation statute
6. _____

7. A legal entity created by either a state or a federal statute authorizing individuals to operate an enterprise
7. _____

8. Another name for a dummy corporation
8. _____

9. A corporation formed in another country
9. _____

10. Stock that carries with it all the risks of doing business
10. _____

Applying the Law

1. Dynasoar, Inc., was incorporated in Delaware and had its principal place of business in New Jersey. The directors of Dynasoar decided to open a branch office and several stores in Mississippi. What legal steps will Dynasoar have to take before opening either the office or the stores?

_____
_____
_____
_____

2. Granger and Hollister have decided to form a limited liability company. Accordingly, they file their articles of organization with the secretary of state, appoint a statutory agent and pay the proper filing fee. Hollister argues that the law now requires the filing of an operating agreement. Granger states that while such a step is desirable, it is not required by law. Which party is correct? Explain.

_____
_____
_____

3. Hayes acted as promoter in the incorporation of the Dry-by-Night Cleaning Company. As part of the process of forming Dry-by-Night, Hayes purchased a delivery van from the Eaton Auto Mall. The effort to incorporate Dry-by-Night failed, and Hayes was forced to pay for the van himself. Why?

_____
_____
_____

4. McKinley, Hinders, and Manning followed all the correct steps in the incorporation process. However, after filing with the secretary of state's office, their papers were lost and a certificate of incorporation was never issued. Never theless, they operated as if they were a corporation. When one of their drivers caused an automobile accident, McKinley, Hinders, and Manning were sued as individuals rather than as a corporation. Identify and explain the doctrine they can use in their defense.

_____

_____

_____

_____

5. Phillips did everything that was necessary under state law to incorporate. However, he continued to un his business as a sole proprietorship and simply used the false corporate front to avoid personal liability on several contracts entered into for personal reasons but in the corporation's name. One of Phillips's creditors decided to disregard the phony corporate front and sue Phillips directly. Identify the legal theory that allowed the creditor to do this.

_____

_____

_____

_____

6. Riley was asked to invest in New Markets. She was told that New Markets was a legally formed corporation; in fact, no incorporation had ever taken place. Later, Riley was asked to become vice-president of New Markets. As part of her job, she ordered the purchase of several computers from Kearney Komputers, Inc. When New Markets failed to pay for the computers and Kearney found out that the corporation did not really exist, Kearney attempted to hold Riley personally liable. Identify the legal doctrine that might protect Riley in this case.

_____

_____

_____

7. Zelek, Inc., was incorporated in Delaware and had its principal place of business in Maryland. Zelek had no holdings in any other states and did business exclusively in Maryland. The Lennons had an auto-mobile accident with a Zelek delivery truck while they were visiting relatives in Maryland. They then returned to Virginia and attempted to sue Zelek in Virginia. Their attempt failed. Why?

_____

_____

_____

_____

8. Enright owned 100 shares of common stock in Antares, Inc. In five years he had received no dividend payments. As a result, he elected to sue Antares, claiming that the directors had a duty to pay dividends at least once every year. Was Enright correct? Explain.

_____

_____

_____

_____

9. Marple and Taft were both shareholders in Radnik, Inc. For two years neither of hem received dividends. In the third year, both received dividends. Marple also received payment for dividends not paid in the previous two years. Taft received no dividends for those years. What type of stock did each shareholder own?

_____

_____

_____

_____

10. The United Federated Loan Company, Inc., loaned $10,000 to Grant. Grant secured the loan with a mortgage on his home. His home was later condemned and destroyed by the county. The loan company received no notice before the demolition and consequently sued the city. What legal principle allowed the loan company to sue the county?

_____

_____

_____

_____

Chapter 39   Corporate Governance

Chapter Outline

**39-1   Management of
         the Corporation**

A. The board of directors is _____
_____
_____

B. The officers of a corporation are _____
_____
_____

C. The corporate shareholders are the _____
_____
_____

**39-2   Issues in
         Corporate
         Governance**

A. Theories of Corporate Governance
    1. Special Interest Group Control is _____
_____
_____

    2. Government Control is _____
_____
_____

    3. Independent Director Control is _____
_____
_____

    4. Managerial Control is _____
_____
_____

    5. Shareholder Control is _____
_____
_____

B. Shareholder Voting Control
    1. Cumulative voting is _____
_____
_____

    2. Proxy solicitation is_____
_____
_____

    3. A voting trust is_____
_____

4. A pooling agreement is _____

_____

_____

5. A shareholder proposal is _____

_____

_____

6. A shareholder nomination is _____

_____

_____

7. Unanimous voting restrictions are_____

_____

_____

C. Shareholder lawsuits

1. A direct suit is _____

_____

2. A derivative suit is_____

_____

39-3 Governance Responsibilities

A. The business judgment rule is _____

_____

B. The fairness rule is_____

_____

1. Insider information is _____

_____

2. The insider trading rule says _____

_____

3. The corporate opportunity doctrine states_____

_____

C. The actual authority rule is _____

_____

1. The duty of obedience is _____

_____

2. Ratification is _____

_____

39-4 Shareholder Rights

A. The right to examine the corporate books involves_____

_____

B. The right to share in dividends means _____

_____

_____

C. The right to transfer stock involves _____

_____

D. Preemptive rights are _____

_____

39-5 Governance of a Limited Liability Company

A. A member-managed LLC is run by _____

_____

B. A manager-managed LLC is managed by _____

_____

C. Both types of managers have a fiduciary duty to _____

_____

Legal Concepts

For each statement, write **T** *in the answer column if the statement is true or* **F** *if the statement is false.*

Answer

1. The people who support the special interest group theory of corporate control believe that only the board of directors should have control over corporate decisions.

   1. _____

2. The people who believe in state control of corporations believe that corporate decisions should be made by an impartial group of outsiders.

   2. _____

3. Members of an LLC can never exercise any management control over the LLC.

   3. _____

4. An outside manager of an LLC never assumes the responsibilities of an agent in relation to that LLC.

   4. _____

5. The outside managers of an LLC owe a fiduciary duty to the LLC, but not to the members of the LLC.

   5. _____

6. Once elected, a director can never resign from a board of directors.

   6. _____

7. Directors must be notified of all regular board meetings.

   7. _____

8. Officers have the authority of general agents for the operation of the normal business of the corporation.

   8. _____

9. The business judgment rule is one way to encourage people to become corporate managers.

   9. _____

10. The fairness rule automatically declares managers to be disloyal if they profit from a corporate decision.

    10. _____

11. Cumulative voting is designed to allow minority shareholders an opportunity to be represented on the board of directors.

    11. _____

12. Only majority shareholders are allowed to solicit proxies.

    12. _____

13. Generally, pooling agreements are interpreted by the court under principles of contract law.

    13. _____

14. Shareholders have the right to sell or transfer their shares of stock.   14. _____
15. Once declared, dividends become a debt of the corporation and are enforceable by law.   15. _____

Language of the Law

Select the legal term that best matches each definition.

a. business judgment rule   **f.** fairness rule   **k.** rule of contemporary ownership
b. corporate democracy   **g.** managerial control   **l.** shareholder proposal
c. cumulative voting   **h.** pooling agreement   **m.** special interest group control
d. derivative suit   **i.** preemptive rights   **n.** state control
e. direct suit   **j.** proxy   **o.** voting trust

                                          Answer

1. The theory that the state, as an impartial third party, should make corporate decisions   1. _____
2. The ability of one shareholder to cast another shareholder's votes   2. _____
3. An agreement among shareholders to transfer their voting rights to a trustee   3. _____
4. A suit brought by shareholders who have been deprived of a right that belongs to them as shareholders   4. _____
5. A shareholder's right to purchase a proportionate share of every new offering of stock by the corporation   5. _____
6. A theory that holds that managers should be more responsive to shareholders   6. _____
7. A system of voting that allows shareholders to multiply the number of their voting shares by the number of directors to be elected   7. _____
8. The rule that holds that in order to institute certain types of lawsuits, shareholders must own stock at the time of the injury and at the time of the suit   8. _____
9. A suit that allows shareholders to sue corporate management on behalf of the corporation because of an injury to the corporation   9. _____
10. A suggestion about a broad company policy or procedure that is submitted by a shareholder   10. _____

Applying the Law

1. Burr was a director on the board of the United Satellite Sales and Service Company. He received no notice of a regularly scheduled board meeting to be held on May 2. At the meeting, a majority of the board voted on several proposals that Burr was opposed to. When he heard about the results of the meeting, he argued that all the actions taken were void because he had received no notice of the meeting. Was Burr correct? Explain.

_____

_____

_____

2. Brickley was chairman of the board and chief executive officer of Adario Industries, Inc. On March 3, several hundred acres of prime timberland, owned by Brinkerhoff, Inc., went on the market. After careful examination of the land, and a detailed study of the corporation's need for the extra acreage, Brickley decided to buy it. The land proved to be less profitable than Brickley had predicted. Name and explain the rule that would protect Brickley should a shareholder question the decision.

_____

_____

_____

_____

3. Chilcote was the chief executive officer of Royalwood Aircraft, Inc. The company was in the market for a new warehouse. Chilcote sold his own warehouse to Royalwood without revealing his owner ship of the building to the board of directors. He also charged Royalwood twice the market value of the warehouse. Identify and explain the rule that will be used to judge Chilcote's behavior.

_____

_____

_____

_____

4. As president of Halvax Construction, Inc., Dunkin knew that Halvax was about to be purchased by Axtel Industries. The purchase would raise the value of Halvax stock by 50 percent. Before the sale and without revealing his knowledge of the impending purchase, Dunkin purchased several hundred shares of Halvax. Identify and explain the rule that will be used to judge Dunkin's conduct.

_____

_____

_____

_____

5. In his role as vice-president of the Brookwood Petroleum Corporation, Diaz learned that several hundred acres of beachfront property were about to go on sale. Diaz knew that this was the same property Brookwood had been interested in purchasing last year. Diaz purchased the property himself and then resold it to the corporation, receiving enormous personal profit. Identify and explain the rule that will be used to judge Diaz's conduct.

_____

_____

_____

_____

6. As a state senator, Harding had proposed a bill in the state legislature that would guarantee minority shareholders a representative on the board of directors in all corporations incorporated in the state. Identify and explain the theory of corporate management that Harding would support.

_____

_____

_____

_____

7. Dittrich, Beal, and Albright were shareholders in Comstock Assemblies, Inc. They orally created a secret voting trust transferring voting rights to Stanley, who agreed to act as trustee. When Beal changed his mind and pulled out of the voting trust, Dittrich and Albright argued that he had no right to break up the trust. Were they correct? Explain.

_____

_____

_____

_____

8. Pollard owned 5 percent of the voting stock of Roanoke Telespectrum Industries, Inc. The market value of the stock was $900. Sixty days before the next shareholders' meeting, Pollard submitted a 750-word shareholder proposal to the directors of Roanoke Telespectrum. The directors rightfully rejected the proposal. Why?

_____

_____

_____

_____

9. Stowe owned several hundred shares of voting stock in the Volk-Studer Cosmetics Corporation. The directors of Volk-Studer declared that dividends would be paid in the first quarter of the following year. When Stowe did not receive her dividends, she filed suit against the directors of Volk-Studer. The directors told her she could not bring suit because she had not exhausted internal remedies first. Were the directors correct? Explain.

_____

_____

_____

10. Higgins owned 200 shares of Fung Communications, Inc. Fung had 600 shares total. Fung decided to increase its capital stock 1,200 shares. Assuming that Higgins elected to exercise his preemptive rights, to how many shares would he be entitled?

_____

_____

_____

Chapter 40   Government Regulation of Corporate Business

Chapter Outline

40-1   Business and   A. The Commerce Clause of the U.S. Constitution states _____
         the Constitution
                              _____

                              _____

                          B. The Judicial-Economic System is empowered by the following
                              factors: _____

                              _____

                              _____

                          C. The regulatory activities of state government are based on_____

                              _____

                              _____

                              _____

40-2   Securities   A. The Securities Act of 1933 regulates_____
         Regulation
                              _____

                              _____

                              _____

                          B. The Securities and Exchange Act of 1934 establishes_____

                              _____

                              _____

                              _____

40-3   Antitrust   A. The Sherman Antitrust Act prohibits_____
         Regulation
                              _____

                              _____

                          B. Post-Sherman Antitrust Legislation
                              1   The Clayton Act polices_____

                              _____

                              _____

                              2. The Robinson-Patman Act deals with _____

                              _____

                              _____

                              3. The Federal Trade Commission Act established_____

                              _____

                              _____

C. The objective of the U.S. Antitrust Modernization Committee is to

_____

_____

40-4 Regulation of Corporate Expansion

A. Expansion Tactics in Mergers and Acquisitions
  1. A merger is_____

  _____

  2. An asset acquisition is _____

  _____

  _____

  3. A stock acquisition is _____

  _____

  _____

B. Expansion Tactics and Antitrust Law
  1. Horizontal expansion occurs _____

  _____

  _____

  2. Vertical expansion occurs _____

  _____

  _____

  3. Conglomerate expansion is _____

  _____

  _____

40-5 Other Forms of Regulation

A. The Federal Energy Regulatory Commission is _____

  _____

  _____

B. The Environmental Protection Agency is _____

  _____

  _____

C. The Employment Retirement Income Security Act requires employers_____

  _____

  _____

40-6 The Government and Corporate Dissolution

A. A _quo warranto_ action is _____

  _____

  _____

B. A corporation can be dissolved voluntarily by _____

  _____

  _____

40-7 **The Dissolution of a Limited Liability Company**

A. The dissolution of a limited liability company can be triggered by

_____

_____

B. Winding up the affairs of an LLC involves_____

_____

_____

Legal Concepts

For each statement, write **T** *in the answer column if the statement is true or* **F** *if the statement is false.*

Answer

1. The regulatory activities of the federal government are based on its police power.

1. _____

2. The Securities and Exchange Commission (SEC) was established by the Securities Act of 1933.

2. _____

3. A prospectus is actually a condensed version of a registration statement.

3. _____

4. Agreements between competitors to divide territories among themselves to minimize competition would be lawful if the agreements help the parties compete against others outside the agreements.

4. _____

5. The Clayton Act outlawed tying agreements but legalized interlocking directorates.

5. _____

6. The Robinson-Patman Act deals with product pricing, advertising, and promotional allowances.

6. _____

7. The SEC is concerned with regulating the expansion of corporations, while the Federal Trade Commission (FTC) is more concerned with the effects of the expansion.

7. _____

8. Today, most legal scholars make no distinction between merger and consolidation.

8. _____

9. In an asset acquisition, the debts of the acquired corporation become liabilities of the acquiring corporation.

9. _____

10. In a stock acquisition, the acquiring corporation deals directly with the shareholders.

10. _____

11. Horizontal mergers are more likely to result in monopolies.

11. _____

12. The Hart-Scott-Rodino Act was designed to police expansion techniques that might harm competition in the marketplace.

12. _____

13. The Environmental Protection Agency is responsible for licensing nuclear power plants.

13. _____

14. If a corporation has repeatedly conducted business in an unlawful manner, the courts can bring a *quo warranto* action against the corporation.

14. _____

15. The government must be informed when a corporation voluntarily dissolves.

15. _____

Language of the Law

Select the legal term that best matches each definition.

a. asset acquisition
b. conglomerate expansion
c. consolidation
d. horizontal expansion
e. junk bonds
f. leveraged buy out
g. prospectus
h. registration statement
i. PRM agreement
j. security
k. suitor
l. takeover
m. target
n. trying agreement
o. vertical expansion

Answer

1. An expansion involving companies that were once in a customer-supplier relationship

1. _____

2. A document that contains detailed information about a corporation, including data about its management, capitalization, and financial condition

2. _____

3. A transaction that involves a group of shareholders that purchase a controlling portion of the stock in a corporation by enlisting the support of a commercial bank and an investment banker

3. _____

4. Investment that expects a return solely due to another's effort

4. _____

5. A transaction in which a seller refuses to sell a given product unless the buyer agrees to buy another product from the seller that is related to the first product

5. _____

6. The purchase of enough voting stock to control a target corporation

6. _____

7. An expansion involving two companies that were not previously in competition with one another

7. _____

8. An agreement that occurs when a retailer and a manufacturer agree that the retailer will sell a product at the price set by the manufacturer

8. _____

9. A corporate expansion technique that involves one corporation purchasing all of the property of another corporation

9. _____

10. A corporation that offers to buy the voting stock of another corporation

10. _____

Applying the Law

1. Roth owned Images and Illusions, Inc., a fashion-design business that specialized in clothing for the very rich. Roth had four of her richest clients sponsor each of her seasonal lines of clothing. Each contributed $1 million and received a return on that contribution based on Roth's profits each year. Roth claimed that this was not a security. Was she correct? Explain.

_____

_____

_____

_____

2. Holley, a shareholder in Mark One, Inc., was dissatisfied with a decision by Mark One's board's refusing to transfer all of its funds from the Newman National Bank to the Maxcorp City Bank. Since Holley did not own enough stock of his own to gain control of the corporation and reverse the decision, he decided to enter a proxy solicitation campaign. When Holley compiled his proxy solicitation material, he mentioned his controlling interest in Maxcorp by placing it in fine print on the last page of the document. The directors of Mark One filed suit to prevent Holley's campaign from going forward. Holley lost the suit. Why?

_____
_____
_____
_____

3. Oslo Enterprises, Inc., and the Karnes Corporation were the two major mail-order houses in the Midwest. To minimize competition, they negotiated an agreement whereby Oslo would handle all the business in Ohio, Michigan, Wisconsin, and Indiana, and Karnes would handle all the business in Minnesota, Iowa, Missouri, and Illinois. Before the agreement was finalized, corporate counsel for Oslo warned that the agreement would violate federal antitrust laws. The attorney for Karnes argued that the agreement would stand because it was reasonable protection against the east-west mail-order houses. Was the attorney for Karnes correct? Explain.

_____
_____
_____
_____

4. Tolliver Floor Care, Inc., manufactured a line of vacuum cleaners which the Varnes Tile Company wanted to market. Tolliver refused to sell the vacuum cleaner to Varnes unless Varnes also agreed to market Tolliver's floor waxers. Varnes properly objected to the stipulation. Explain.

_____
_____
_____

5. Strickland, a shareholder in Maxwell Dental Supplies, Inc., objected to the corporation's recent asset acquisition of Crown Dental Equipment, Inc. Strickland argued that the asset acquisition was invalid because the directors had not obtained permission from Maxwell's stockholders. Was Strickland correct? Explain.

_____

_____

_____

6. Schuler wanted to purchase Coleman-Walters, Inc. When he approached the board of directors about a merger, they told him they were not interested. Schuler then suggested an asset acquisition. Again the board refused. What measure could Schuler take to sidestep the board of directors in order to obtain control of Coleman-Walters?

_____

_____

_____

7. Refer back to the previous question and consider these additional facts: Schuler elected to follow the alternative means of acquiring Coleman-Walters and the board of directors intended to fight him. What could the board do to fight Schuler's actions?

_____

_____

_____

8. Remy Industries, Inc., purchased all the assets of the Renaissance Landscape Corporation. Remy then proceeded to sell some of those assets while retaining others. The Saunders Nursery claimed that Renaissance owed the nursery several thousand dollars. When Saunders discovered that Remy had purchased the assets of Renaissance, Saunders attempted to recover the debt from Remy. Saunders was unsuccessful. Why?

_____

_____

_____

9. The Dunlap-Winston Petroleum Corporation purchased a storage facility on the banks of the Monongahela River. After filling the storage tanks on the river with crude oil, Dunlap-Winston discovered several structural weaknesses in the tanks. Before the company could act, several thousand gallons of crude oil spilled into the river. The United States sued Dunlap-Winston for violating federal pollution laws. Dunlap-Winston argued that it should not be liable because the pollution was unintentional. Was Dunlap-Winston correct? Explain.

_____

_____

_____

10. Yetzer Delivery Service, Inc., was properly incorporated under the appropriate state statute. Nevertheless, Yetzer had not paid any franchise taxes nor had the corporation filed annual reports. Yetzer had also failed to maintain a registered agent for service of process as is required by state law. What could the state do about this situation?

_____

_____

_____

Chapter 41   Professional Liability

Chapter Outline

41-1   The Liability   **A.** An accountant is_____
of Accountants   _____
                                   _____

                        B. Accountant Registration
                                1. A certified public accountant (CPA) is _____
                                        _____
                                        _____

                                2. A public accountant (PA) is _____
                                        _____
                                        _____

                        C. Accounting and Auditing
                                1. An accountant performs the following tasks:_____
                                        _____

                                2. An auditor is_____
                                        _____
                                        _____

                        D. The Sarbanes-Oxley Act created the _____
                                _____
                                _____

                        E. The person who suffers when accountants clash with other
                                professionals is the_____
                                _____

                        F. An accountant might be liable to clients under common law for
                                1. _____
                                        _____

                                2. _____
                                        _____

                        G. Under common law, accountants are liable to third parties who
                                _____
                                _____

                        H. Accountants can be held liable for violating the following statutes
                                1. _____
                                2. _____
                                3. _____

41-2   **The Liability of Architects and Attorneys**

     A. An architect is _____
_____
_____

        1. The architects' standard of care requires that _____
_____
_____

        2. The cost of repair rule holds that _____
_____
_____

     B. An attorney is _____
_____
_____

        1. An attorney has the duty to represent his or her clients with
           a. _____
           b. _____
           c. _____
        2. Attorneys are rarely held liable to third parties because _____
_____
_____

41-3   **The Liability of Health Care Professionals**

     A. Health care providers are _____
_____
_____

     B. Determining how the reasonable health care provider would act in a given situation can be determined by reference to
        1. _____
        2. _____
        3. _____
        4. _____
        5. _____

     C. Congress ensured the protection of medical records when it passed
_____

41-4   **Hospital Liability**

     A. In the medical setting ostensible authority is created when _____
_____
_____

     B. Negligent credentialing occurs _____
_____

     C. Tort reform has been instituted in hospital ostensible authority in order to _____
_____

Legal Concepts

For each statement, write **T** *in the answer column if the statement is true or* **F** *if the statement is false.*

Answer

1. The only job of an accountant is to keep financial records for his or her clients.

   1. _____

2. The state cannot prevent someone from practicing accounting as a profession.

   2. _____

3. An auditor is a guarantor of an institution's financial records.

   3. _____

4. Auditing standards explain how an auditor can determine whether proper accounting procedures have been used.

   4. _____

5. According to the accounting profession's Code of Professional Ethics, an accountant cannot reveal information about a client's business to anyone, even ordered to do so by a court of law.

   5. _____

6. An accountant can never be held liable to third parties who might be damaged by a negligently prepared financial statement.

   6. _____

7. Accountants cannot be found liable for violating state blue sky laws.

   7. _____

8. Under its police power, the state can regulate the conduct of architects.

   8. _____

9. The standard of care requires an architect to use the same methods, techniques, and procedures that an architect of ordinary skill would use in a similar situation.

   9. _____

10. Architects, like all other professionals, are held liable for all mistakes made while on the job.

    10. _____

11. Attorneys must have one year of on-the-job experience before they can practice law.

    11. _____

12. If an attorney fails to act in the best interests of a client, the attorney faces a potential lawsuit brought by the client and potential disciplinary action brought by the state.

    12. _____

13. An attorney can represent two clients on opposite sides of the same dispute as long as both sides consent to the dual representation.

    13. _____

14. Informed consent must be in writing on a form signed by the patient and witnessed by a third party.

    14. _____

15. Determining how a reasonable health care professional would act in a given situation can be decided only by reference to the policy or procedure manual.

    15. _____

Language of the Law

Select the legal term that best matches each definition.

a. Adverse opinion
b. audit
c. certified public accountant (CPA)
d. Code of Professional Ethics
e. disclaimer

f. general consent
g. generally accepted accounting principles (GAAP)
h. generally accepted auditing standards (GAAS)
i. locality rule

j. national standard
k. professional
l. public accountant (PA)
m. qualified opinion
n. similar locality rule
o. unqualified opinion

Answer

1. An accountant who has met certain age, character, education, experience, and testing requirements

1. _____

2. Rules that outline the procedures that accountants must use in accumulating financial data and in preparing financial statements

2. _____

3. An opinion issued by an auditor that concludes that the records of a company are an accurate reflection of the company's financial status

3. _____

4. An individual who can perform a highly specialized task because of his or her special abilities, education, experience, and knowledge

4. _____

5. An examination of the financial records of an organization to determine whether those records are a fair presentation of the actual financial health of the organization

5. _____

6. A declaration that states that an auditor had decided not to give any opinion on a company's financial records

6. _____

7. A standard that judges a health care provider's behavior based on how other health care professionals in the same community would have acted

7. _____

8. An opinion issued by an auditor when the financial statements do not fairly represent the financial health of the organization

8. _____

9. The rule that compares rural hospitals to rural hospitals, urban hospitals to urban hospitals, and suburban hospitals to suburban hospitals when determining the liability of a health care provider

9. _____

10. Consent given the moment a patient enters a hospital setting

10. _____

Applying the Law

1. Webber was neither a CPA nor a PA. Despite this fact, she opened an office and advertised that she would perform bookkeeping services at reasonable rates. Banner told Webber that she could not provide such services without first becoming either a CPA or a PA. Why was Banner's statement inaccurate?

_____

_____

_____

_____

2. Curtis was hired to audit the books of the Baumann Corporation. When he was finished with his work, Curtis issued an opinion that stated that the books represented the company's health as of the date of the completion of the audit. Curtis added that a lawsuit pending against Baumann could affect the company's health. Identify the type of opinion that Curtis issued in this case.

_____

_____

_____

_____

3. Baird was hired to audit the books of the Hatch Company. After completing her work, Baird issued an opinion that said that the Hatch Company bookkeeper had consistently ignored generally accepted accounting principles and had failed to disclose some very important financial information. What kind of an opinion had Baird issued?

_____

_____

_____

_____

4. Gibson was hired by Houston to prepare a financial statement about Houston's business. Houston told Gibson that she wanted the financial statement to convince McCoy to invest in her business. Gibson made several crucial errors in the statement because he failed to use the same skill and competence that a reasonable accounting professional would use in a similar situation. McCoy relied on the statement and lost a great deal of money as a result. Why would Gibson be liable to McCoy even though McCoy was not his client?

_____

_____

_____

_____

5. Jameson was the regular accountant for Lakeview Industries, Inc. Noll, the president of Lakeview, asked Jameson to develop an extra set of financial records that would indicate that Lakeview was much healthier than it actually was. Jameson did as Noll asked. Metcalf, an investor, was misled by the information and lost a great deal of money. When Metcalf named Jameson in a lawsuit, Jameson argued that since Metcalf was not a client or a named third party, she could not bring the suit against him. Was Jameson correct? Explain.

_____

_____

_____

_____

6. Podmore was the architect who had worked on plans for the new Monroe City Library. Podmore had made several mistakes in calculating how much weight a balcony in the library could hold. Jefferson, the contractor, ignored Podmore's plans and made his own calculations, which also proved to be incorrect. When the books were moved onto the balcony, it collapsed under the weight. Podmore argued that she should not be held liable. Was she correct? Explain.

_____

_____

_____

7. Renkar, an attorney, was hired by Stover to act as his agent as he negotiated a new contract with the Cutler City Comets, a professional soccer team. Unknown to Stover, Renkar was also on the board of directors of the Cutler City Comets. What duty did Renkar violate in this situation?

_____

_____

_____

8. Zent acted as York's attorney in York's suit against his former employer, the Albert Restaurant Chain of America, Inc. York was fighting a contractual clause that would have prevented him from working as a chef for any of Albert's competitors for two years. When York won the case, Albert sued Zent for helping York in his fight to retain his position as chef for the Carmine Restaurant Chain. Albert's suit failed. Explain.

_____

_____

_____

9. Passarelli entered Cumberland County General Hospital for several diagnostic x-rays. Before taking the x-rays, Dr. DeLong had to inject Passarelli with a contrast medium. To save time and trouble, DeLong told Passarelli that the consent form was an insurance form. When Passarelli had an adverse reaction to the contrast medium, he sued DeLong and the hospital for battery. Why won't the consent form protect DeLong or the hospital?

_____

_____

_____

10. Brodsky was a patient at Shields Memorial Hospital; Quinn was a nurse at Sheilds. While Brodsky was out of the room, Quinn accidentally spilled a pitcher of water on the floor of Brodsky's room. Before cleaning up the mess, Quinn took her lunch break. When Brodsky returned to his room, he slipped in the puddle of water, fell, and injured himself. Brodsky sued Quinn and the hospital for negligence. At the trial, Brodsky argued that there was no need for an expert witness to testify as to the standards of care rendered by the nurse. Was Brodsky correct? Explain.

_____

_____

_____

Chapter 42   Electronic Law

Chapter Outline

42-1   Electronic Crimes

A. Electronic Crimes and E-Trespass
  1. An electronic crime is _____
      _____
      _____
      _____

  2. E-trespass is _____
      _____
      _____

B. Electronic Crimes Executed with Computers
  1. Electronic extortion is _____
      _____
      _____
      _____

  2. Electronic stalking involves_____
      _____
      _____

  3. In electronic spoofing, the perpetrator uses _____
      _____
      _____

  4. Electronic piracy involves _____
      _____
      _____

C. Electronic Crimes that Focus on Computers
  1. Electronic terrorism includes_____
      _____
      _____

  2. In identity theft the electronic criminal steals _____
      _____
      _____

  3. Electronic vandalism is _____
      _____
      _____

  4. Electronic germ warfare involves perpetrators who _____
      _____
      _____

42-2 Electronic Torts

    A. An electronic tort can be described as _____

    _____

    B. Electronic defamation is _____

    _____

    C. An electronic invasion of privacy results from _____

    _____

    D. Private Privacy versus Public Privacy
        1. Private-private information includes _____

        _____

        2. The public-privacy principle is based on the following two suppositions _____

        _____

    E. Data mining occurs when _____

    _____

    F. Statutory Protections and Violations of Privacy
        1. The Fair Credit Reporting Act involves _____

        _____

        2. The Right to Financial Privacy Act forbids_____

        _____

        3. The Electronic Communications Privacy Act was designed to _____

        _____

        4. The Driver's Privacy Protection Act was added _____

        _____

        5. The USA Patriot Act involves_____

        _____

        _____

        6. The Computer Fraud and Abuse Act is _____

        _____

    G. The European Data Protection Directive assures citizens of Europe that_____

    _____

42-3 Electronic Contract Law

    A. The E-Sign Act was instigated by Congress as _____

    _____

    B. The Uniform Electronic Transactions Act makes certain that

    _____

    _____

C. The Uniform Computer Information Transactions Act handles such diverse agreements as _____

_____

42-4 Intellectual Property Rights and Cyberprotection Law

A. A trade mark is _____

_____

B. A trade secret is _____

_____

C. A copyright is _____

_____

D. A patent is _____

_____

Legal Concepts

For each statement, write **T** *in the answer column if the statement is true or* **F** *if the statement is false.*

Answer

1. Electronic law is *sui generis*.   1. _____
2. Electronic law is completely autonomous.   2. _____
3. Only one single way exists in the law to deal with electronic crime.   3. _____
4. Electronic trespass is the use of a computer as an instrumentality to commit a crime.   4. _____
5. Electronic trespass does not include crimes that target a computer as the victim.   5. _____
6. Electronic torts are always somehow entangled with information.   6. _____
7. Electronic spoofing is a harmless prank carrying no criminal penalties. 7. _____
8. Private-privacy and public-privacy are essentially the same thing.   8. _____
9. Data mining is harmless.   9. _____
10. The Right to Financial Privacy Act protects the privacy of the records held by financial institutions.   10. _____
11. The USA Patriot Act discourages surveillance by federal law enforcement agencies.   11. _____
12. The United States and the European Union have taken the same approach to privacy and the computer.   12. _____
13. The Uniform Computer Information Transactions Act is a default statute.   13. _____
14. The Uniform Trade Secrets Act has been declared unconstitutional.   14. _____
15. The Economic Espionage Act created a civil cause of action for corporate spying with a computer.   15. _____

Language of the Law

Select the legal term that best matches each definition.

a. computer law
b. data mining
c. default statute
d. electronic commerce
e. electronic defamation
f. electronic germ warfare

g. electronic piracy
h. electronic stalking
i. electronic terrorism
j. electronic vandalism
k. licensing agreement

l. peer-to-peer networking
m. phishing
n. public-private information
o. trademark
p. trademark tapping

				Answer
1.	Placing two or more pieces of public information together to create information that the victim would consider private		**1.**	_____
2.	An electronic crime in which the perpetrator disrupts an entire computer system		**2.**	_____
3.	A crime that occurs when a hacker targets an innocent person by tracking that person's computer records in order to victimize that innocent person		**3.**	_____
4.	A crime that involves sending out phony e-mails that solicit buyers and in the process obtains private financial records such as credit card information		**4.**	_____
5.	Using viruses to enter and destroy a computer system		**5.**	_____
6.	The tort committed when false and destructive information is transmitted by computer		**6.**	_____
7.	Hybrid information that embarrasses, disturbs or financially injures an innocent party		**7.**	_____
8.	An agreement under which the user of a computer product promises to respect the program owner's desire for secrecy		**8.**	_____
9.	A technique used to increase the number of "hits" on a website		**9.**	_____
10.	Another term used for electronic law, e-law, and cyberlaw.		**10.**	_____

Applying the Law

1. The Bradley Electronics Corporation developed a new computer program that would help consumers prepare their tax returns under the new federal income tax law. The program was marketed for wide distribution in a software labeled "Taxes 'R' Fun." Explain why Bradley Electronics would not be able to claim that their new product is a trade secret.

_____

_____

_____

_____

Name_____ Date_____

2. Product design engineers at Nutech Concepts, Inc., developed a new process for destroying certain types of dangerous chemical pollutants. Part of the process had to be controlled by a computer, following the directions of a computer program. This part of the process was only about 20 percent of the entire operation. The patent examiner denied Nutech's request for a patent on the process. A federal court reversed the refusal. Why?

_____

_____

_____

_____

3. Jefferson developed a computer program that allowed instructors to input student test results into a computer. The program allowed the computer to store the students' results and figure out their final grades. Essentially, the program allowed the computer to serve as a memory aid and calculator for the instructor. The patent office correctly refused to grant Jefferson's patent. Why?

_____

_____

_____

4. George Taylor purchased several software packages on the Internet from the Hilliard Book Shop. The software was supposed to help consumers learn how to play poker, bridge, twenty-one, and several other card games. When the software packages failed to work properly, Taylor contacted Hilliard, but was told that, since the contract was made online, it could not be enforced, especially using UCC provisions. Was Hilliard correct? Explain.

_____

_____

_____

_____

5. In a jurisdiction recognizing electronic trespass, Jeremy used his personal computer at work to transfer several thousand dollars from the company's bank accounts into his personal checking account. When he was arrested and charged with embezzlement, Jeremy argued that since there was no such thing as computer embezzle-ment in his state, he could not be tried for em-bezzlement. Is Jeremy correct? Explain.

_____

_____

_____

_____

6. Because he had not paid his water bill for six months, the city water company told Jason that his water would be shut off on Monday. On Sunday afternoon, Jason used his computer to enter the computer system of the city's water department and transmit a virus that destroyed the financial records of the department. When the virus was traced to him, Jason argued that he could not be charged with electronic terrorism because no one had been physically hurt by his actions. Is Jason correct? Explain.

_____

_____

_____

_____

7. After she was fired, Carol used her expertise to enter the computer system of Harrington Industries in order to make certain that the entire system crashed. When she was uncovered as the source of Harrington's problem, she said that she could not be charged with electronic vandalism because she had not personally gained from engineering the crash of Harrington's computer system. Is Carol correct? Explain.

_____

_____

_____

_____

8. Nick has just returned from a seminar in Paris during which he learned about thecomputer privacy directives issued by the European Union. Nick tells Amy that he is certain that he now understands not only the EU directives but also privacy in the USA because the two privacy programs are identical. Amy disagrees. Who is correct, Nick or Amy? Explain.

_____

_____

_____

9. Sam has monopolized the domain name of Harry's Ham and Eggs, a national chain of restaurants that specialize in all day breakfasts. Sam plans to sell the rights to the domain name to Harry's for 1 million dollars. When Veronica finds out,she warns Sam that his actions are illegal. Sam tells her that she is incorrect because there is no law that deals with premeditated cyber-squatting. Who is correct? Sam or Veronica? Explain.

_____

_____

_____

10. Ben, the CEO of Georgetown Supplies, Inc., just discovered that his former partner, Ken, downloaded all of the company's trade secrets. Ken then sold all of those secrets to Philly Supply and Storage. Ben decides to sue Ken and Philly under the Economic Espionage Act. What will prevent Ben from carrying out his plan? Explain.

_____

_____

_____

Chapter 43   International Law

Chapter Outline

43-1 International Law and the New World Order

A. A new world order is_____
_____
_____

B. The Westphalia System describes_____
_____
_____

C. The Post 9/11 New World Order Theories include:
1. _____
2. _____
3. _____
4. _____

43-2 International Law and the Waging of War

A. The Just War Theory endorses six criteria for evaluating the morality of a given war:
1. _____
2. _____
3. _____
4. _____
5. _____
6. _____

B. Preemptive war is _____
_____
_____

C. Preemptive war can rarely be justified under the Just War Theory for several reasons:
1. _____
_____
2. _____
_____
3. _____
_____

D. Discussing preemptive war in relation to the four new world order theories reveals _____
_____
_____

E. The Geneva Conventions are _____

_____

_____

_____

43-3 International Law and the United Nations

A. The governing bodies of the UN are _____

_____

_____

B. The International Law Commission is _____

_____

_____

C. The International Court of Justice is made of _____

_____

D. The International Criminal Court was established in _____

_____

E. The UN Commission on International Trade Law consists of ____

_____

F. The UN Convention on Contracts for the International Sale of Goods applies _____

_____

_____

G. Additional UN Economic Agencies include _____

_____

H. The Division for Science and Technology was created _____

_____

I. The Economic Security Council would _____

_____

_____

43-4 International Law, Finance, and Trade

A. The mission of the World Bank is _____

_____

_____

B. The World Trade Organization was designed to _____

_____

_____

C. NAFTA is _____

_____

_____

D. In the European Union, the use of the euro is designed to _____

_____

_____

_____

Legal Concepts

For each statement, write **T** *in the answer column if the statement is true*   **Answer**
or **F** *if the statement is false.*

1. Historically, the first use of the phrase "new world order" was by George H. W. Bush during the invasion of Iraq in 1991.   1. _____

2. The phrase "new world order" describes how nation states relate to one another on a global scale.   2. _____

3. Under the Westphalia system, the primary actors on the international scene are non-governmental organizations, such as the United Nations.   3. _____

4. The Just War Theory provides criteria for determining when it is morally acceptable to enter a war, but does not involve any standards for waging war or for the behavior following a war.   4. _____

5. A preemptive war is waged to stop another nation-state from reaching a point at which it is capable of attacking another nation-state..   5. _____

6. The Geneva Conventions do not apply to the United States.   6. _____

7. The Security Council of the UN deals with crises that involve threats to international peace.   7. _____

8. Individuals are permitted to bring cases to the International Court of Justice.   8. _____

9. The UN Economic Security Council was established in 1948.   9. _____

10. The World Bank and the International Monetary Fund are two names for the same institution.   10. _____

11. The World Trade Organization replaced the General Agreement on Tarrifs and Trade.   11. _____

12. Under WTO standards, the principle of most-favored nation status has been abolished.   12. _____

13. The European Union has been unable to establish a common currency.   13. _____

14. The European Union has ignored cybercommerce.   14. _____

15. NAFTA is a trade agreement involving the United States, Canada, and Mexico.   15. _____

Language of the Law

Select the legal term that best matches each definition.

a. civilization
b. euro
c. General Assembly
d. Geneva Conventions

e. Just War Theory
f. most-favored nation principle
g. North American Free Trade Agreement

h. Secretariat
i. Secretary General
j. Security Council
k. Westphalia system

Answer

1. The chief administrator of the United Nations
   1. _____

2. The theory used to determine the morality of a war.
   2. _____

3. The administrative bureaucracy of the United Nations
   3. _____

4. The system that identifies the nation-state as the main actor on the international scene
   4. _____

5. A group of people in a series of different nation-states that share certain common characteristics
   5. _____

6. The principle that states that all members of the WTO must treat all other member nations in the same way in relation to similar imports
   6. _____

7. The body that is made up of all of the nations that belong to the United Nations
   7. _____

8. A set of standards adopted after World War II to address many problems brought on by war
   8. _____

9. The United Nations body that deals with international crises
   9. _____

10. The common currency used in the European Union
   10. _____

Applying the Law

1. A United Nations peacekeeper on a mission in central Europe was kidnapped by government agents. The peacekeeper's home nation filed a grievance with the International Court of Justice. The nation that held the peacekeeper as a prisoner objected, arguing that only the UN Security Council can take cases to the ICJ. Is this correct or is it legally permissible for such a case to be filed by a nation-state?

_____

_____

_____

_____

2. The International Law Commission of the United Nations presented a new convention on diplomacy to the General Assembly. The General Assembly voted to approve the new convention. The new convention was then codified as the new UN Convention on Diplomacy and Global Relations. When Alfred Georgiana, a UN representative, objected to the convention, O'Donnell, one of the newest members of the UN legal team, indicated that, while Georgiana's objection was duly noted, the nation in question would still have to obey the rules of that convention. Is O'Donnell correct?

_____

_____

_____

_____

3. Jen-Luc deBroglie, a citizen of France, placed an order for several pieces of expensive pottery from the Austrian firm of Vienna Pottery, Ltd. When the pottery arrived, it was badly damaged during shipping. When Jean-Luc tells his friend Pierre de Chardin, Pierre tells Jean-Luc that he is out of luck because the Directive on the Protection of Consumers in Respect of Distance Contracts (ECD) will not protect him. Is Pierre correct? Explain.

_____

_____

_____

_____

4. Transglobal Airlines was transporting a cargo of fruits and vegetables for the United States government to the Middle East when a terrorist attack shut down all airports in the country of Saudi Arabia, the final destination of the trip. While Transglobal had to wait out the delay, it placed the cargo in special refrigeration units. The use of the units cost the company an extra $50,000. When the government refused to pay the extra amount, Transglobal brought suit. Will the airline win the case? Explain.

_____

_____

_____

_____

5. Quentin was assigned to write a paper justifying the American invasion of Iraq in 2003 under the Just War Theory. Which of the six categories fail to justify the war? Which of the categories can be used to justify the war? Explain.

_____

_____

_____

_____

6. Maria Hegel, a citizen of Germany, has discovered that Chardin, Ltd., has been disseminating computer data about her financial records that is not correct. As a citizen of the European Union, does she have any course of action here? Explain.

_____

_____

_____

_____

7. Friedrich and Francois are involved in a heated argument about the adoption of the euro in the EU. Francois says that all member states must adopt the euro, but Friedrich says that this is not so. Who is correct here? Why?

_____

_____

_____

_____

8. Isabella had a contract with a German company for the delivery of several automobiles. When the company failed to deliver, Isabella indicated that she intended to bring her case to the International Court of Justice. Can Isabella make good on her claim? Explain.

_____

_____

_____

_____

9. The United States claimed that Mexico had violated a treaty between the two countries that related to the right to fish in each country's territorial waters. The United States threatened to bring the case to the International Court of Justice. Mexico said that the ICJ did not have jurisdiction. Which country is correct? Explain.

_____

_____

_____

_____

10. While in the Middle East on a peace keeping mission, several British soldiers were killed. The UK intends to ask the International Court of Justice for an advisory opinion in the case. Can the ICJ issue such an opinion? Explain.

_____

_____

_____

_____

KEY

Chapter 1
Ethical Concepts

1.	T	6.	F	11.	F
2.	T	7.	T	12.	T
3.	F	8.	T	13.	T
4.	T	9.	F	14.	T
5.	F	10.	T	15.	T

Language of the Law

1.	c	6.	g
2.	h	7.	a
3.	f	8.	i
4.	d	9.	k
5.	e	10.	l

Applying the Law
1. Muller is using subjective ethics, which claims that there are no constant and unchanging standards of right and wrong.
2. Tuttle has been neither compassionate nor fair. He has not been sympathetic to others and he does not seem to have any sense of justice.
3. Karu is ignoring the character trait of honesty. He is showing his daughter that he would cheat his company.
4. LaRue is using the character trait of compassion.
5. Alonso is ignoring the character trait of compassion.
6. Gunderson has violated the character trait of honesty because she has failed to reveal the complete truth about her activities during her previous employment.
7. Lowell has violated the principle of justice because, instead of treating people fairly and equally, she has decided to use her own personal preferences in deciding on the layoffs.
8. The board can use the following arguments: (a) the corporation has been granted certain legal advantages that require corporate social responsibility; (b) corporate decisions have a wide impact; (c) corporations should follow enlightened self-interest.
9. Harrington has used compassion here; he has also followed the Golden Rule.
10. Hackett is using the Golden Rule, which is a principle that demands that we respect others.

Chapter 2
Legal Concepts

1.	F	6.	F	11.	F
2.	F	7.	F	12.	F
3.	T	8.	T	13.	F
4.	F	9.	T	14.	F
5.	T	10.	T	15.	F

Language of the Law

1.	i	6.	j
2.	e	7.	m
3.	b	8.	l
4.	f	9.	n
5.	c	10.	a

Applying the Law
1. Dennison was wrong because a ruling by the supreme court within a state would be binding on all lower state courts within that state.
2. Wesleyan was wrong because Congress has enacted the Administration Procedures Act which controls the activities of federal agencies such as the FCC.
3. LaForge was incorrect because a uniform code such as the UCC does not become law in a given jurisdiction until it is adopted by the appropriate legislative body within that jurisdiction.
4. Kenilson was wrong because courts do have to rely on precedent when interpreting a statute.
5. The public defender is correct. The power and the duty to control the right of free

speech in relation to public employees has devolved to the state.

6. The sheriff was incorrect because the 14th Amendment has been interpreted by the courts to require the states, and all governmental subdivisions of the states, to guarantee the same rights that are guaranteed by the federal government in the Bill of Rights.

7. The Viking lawyers were incorrect because both states have adopted the UCC.

8. Loeb was incorrect because cases decided by the California courts would have only persuasive authority in Wyoming.

9. Article 6 of the United States Constitution contains the Supremacy Clause, which states that all statutes must be in line with the principles established by the U.S. Constitution.

10. Werner was wrong because the courts do have the power to interpret statutes.

Chapter 3
Legal Concepts

1.	T	6.	T	11.	T
2.	F	7.	F	12.	T
3.	F	8.	F	13.	F
4.	F	9.	F	14.	F
5.	F	10.	T	15.	F

Language of the Law

1.	e	6.	f
2.	m	7.	l
3.	j	8.	k
4.	b	9.	i
5.	c	10.	g

Applying the Law

1. Morgan is correct. Lynch can have the case removed to federal court provided he can show that the case belonged in federal court in the first place.

2. Franklin was correct because the minimum amount in controversy in federal court is $75,000.

3. Bunker was incorrect because, when a federal court hears a diversity case, the court must apply the law of the state in which it is physically located.

4. Queen's attorney is correct because only parties can be required to submit to interrogatories.

5. Bogan cannot be dismissed because his financial interest in the case was too remote.

6. Cascio's fears were unfounded because witnesses do not appear in appellate courts.

7. Janeway can obtain a writ of execution requiring Kirk's property to be sold by the sheriff to satisfy the judgment.

8. Bernard is not correct because a plea is entered at the arraignment.

9. Tupperman is incorrect because jury proceedings are held in secret.

10. Krauss is incorrect because the prosecution has the burden of proof in a criminal trial.

Chapter 4
Legal Concepts

1.	T	6.	T	11.	F
2.	T	7.	T	12.	F
3.	T	8.	F	13.	F
4.	F	9.	F	14.	T
5.	F	10.	T	15.	F

Language of the Law

1.	b	6.	k
2.	e	7.	m
3.	o	8.	n
4.	g	9.	c
5.	a	10.	j

Applying the Law

1. Jansen may suggest submitting the dispute to arbitration so that the parties have the opportunity to choose at least one engineering expert to serve as an arbitrator.

2. The plan would favor Krenshaw who, as a free-lance artist, would not have the financial resources to take a case to trial.

3. The Thompsons are incorrect. The courts have consistently held that mandatory arbitration is not constitutional as long as it does not eliminate a party's right to trial.

4. Yes, this is the type of situation that is appropriate for a reg-neg approach. The reg-neg approach is designed to create a cooperative process by which all the parties affected by a new agency rule (or by a modification of an existing set of agency rules) have the chance to shape the final form that the rule(s) will take.

5. A science court might also handle the type of situation outlined in Question 4. However, it is difficult to determine which approach would be better of the two. One advantage to the science court is that such a court would be run by a panel of objective judges with diverse scientific backgrounds who would provide a neutral body capable of making unbiased, but well-informed decisions.

6. Yes. The failure of the arbitrator to follow the detailed requirements of the ADR clause would be grounds for the court to revoke the arbitrator's ruling.

7. The ADR alternatives available to Olsen and the city include arbitration, mediation, early neutral evaluation, a summary jury trial, and a private civil trial.

8. The Nebraska Department of Transportation could engage in the reg-neg procedure.

9. Yes. A science court could handle this situation. A science court would provide a neutral body capable of making unbiased, but well-informed judgments that would help decide the dispute.

10. Danza and Maxwell would probably agree to settle the case out of court. Maxwell will want to settle now because there are indications that the company will lose the case if it goes to trial. Danza would favor a settlement because, although there are indications that he might win the case, there are also indications that he may not receive an adequate amount of damages.

Chapter 5
Legal Concepts

1. T	6. F	11. F
2. F	7. T	12. F
3. F	8. F	13. T
4. T	9. T	14. T
5. F	10. T	15. F

Language of the Law

1. e	6. g
2. h	7. i
3. j	8. f
4. k	9. a
5. b	10. d

Applying the Law

1. Conrad was incorrect. To succeed, the defendant using the entrapment defense must demonstrate that he or she would not have committed the crime had he or she not been enticed to do so by a law enforcement official. Here, Conrad was already engaged in an illegal fencing operation before the police got involved.

2. Rainier's self defense claim will succeed if he can demonstrate that he was in fear of death or severe bodily harm, that he did not start the altercation, and that he used only enough force to repel the attack.

3. McArthur did not commit the criminal act of theft because her mistake negated her knowledge of wrongdoing, a necessary element of the crime.

4. Jenkins committed voluntary manslaughter.

5. Newton cannot use mistake as a defense in this case because his mistake did not negate any of the necessary elements of the crime.

6. It is not a valid defense to embezzlement for a criminal defendant to argue that he or she intended to return all of the embezzled money.
7. No. The police did not comply with the request because involuntary behavior like sleepwalking cannot qualify as an act in criminal law.
8. Morris is not correct because the nature of the crime is in the offering of the bribe. Accepting the bribe is another offense altogether.
9. Schmitt is incorrect because simply inserting the stick to enter the open window constitutes an illegal entry.
10. Magill may be charged with a crime depending upon his mental state. In this case, it could be argued that he was either reckless or negligent because he did not check to see whether the revolver was loaded before cleaning it in the presence of another person.

Chapter 6
Legal Concepts

1. T	6. F	11. F
2. T	7. F	12. T
3. F	8. F	13. T
4. F	9. F	14. F
5. F	10. T	15. F

Language of the Law

1. l	6. g
2. a	7. e
3. j	8. i
4. b	9. g
5. h	10. c

Applying the Law

1. No. An assault involves the creation of the immediate apprehension of imminent bodily harm. It requires no actual touching.
2. Yes. Storeowners must be very careful about detaining suspected shoplifters, because such a detention could result in a false imprisonment lawsuit if not handled properly. While most states have laws that allow storekeepers to detain a suspected shoplifter if they have reasonable grounds to suspect that shoplifting has occurred, storekeepers must detain the suspect in a reasonable manner and for no longer than a reasonable length of time.
3. No. The motive of a person who releases the confidential information does not matter. It is still an invasion of privacy.
4. Because the statements printed by Evans about Erickson were false, and because Erickson was hurt by the publication of this false information, Erickson can bring a defamation suit against Evans. Since the false statements were in permanent form, the defamation suit would be considered libel rather than slander.
5. Yes. Fuller has assumed the risk of being hit by a foul ball in Gardner's stadium. Assumption of the risk involves the voluntary exposure by the victim to a known risk. If the injured party was aware of the danger involved in a situation and by his or her actions indicated a willingness to be exposed to the danger then he or she has assumed that risk. An awareness of the extent of the danger is the court's primary consideration in awarding or denying damages. Fuller did not assume the risk of falling out of the upper deck because of a poorly maintained ramp.
6. To determine if Giordano has met the standard of care, the court uses the reasonable person test. This test compares the actions of the tortfeasor with those of the reasonable person in a similar situation. If the reasonable person would not have done what the tortfeasor actually did, then the tortfeasor is liable. The reasonable person is an objective test. Circumstances may change but the reasonable person does not. How the reasonable person would behave in one set of circumstances may not be the same in another set of circumstances.

7. Product liability is a legal theory used here. It imposes liability on the manufacturer and seller of a product produced and sold in a defective condition. Anyone who produces or sells a product in a defective condition (unreasonably dangerous to the user or to the consumer or the property) is subject to liability for the physical or the emotional injury to the ultimate consumer and for any physical harm to the user's property. The courts have regularly held that liability for a defective product extends to the producer of the product, the wholesaler, and the retailer. The seller or producer must be engaged in the business of selling such products. In addition, the product manufactured or sold must be expected to reach the ultimate consumer without substantial change in conditions under which it was originally manufactured or sold. Since evidence indicated that the hair dryer was unreasonably dangerous and since it had reached Wilkinson without being changed in any way, she will win her case against both Frederickson and Milligan.

8. No. He owes a duty of due care to the pedestrians.

9. Yes. Negligence requires actual harm.

10. No. When one party prevents another party from moving about freely, the first party has committed the intentional tort of false imprisonment. The victim of false imprisonment need not be locked in a prison or a jail cell. All that is required is that the person's freedom of movement is restricted in some fashion.

Chapter 7
Legal Concepts

1. F	6. F	11. T
2. F	7. T	12. T
3. T	8. F	13. F
4. T	9. F	14. T
5. T	10. T	15. F

Language of the Law

1. d	6. e
2. I	7. m
3. F	8. a
4. C	9. b
5. J	10. n

Applying the Law

1. Yes. Article 2 of the UCC covers sale of good contracts.
2. No. Gerard is not a party to the contract and thus cannot bring a lawsuit.
3. Yes. Under the terms of implied-in-law contracts, James will have to pay the clinic the fair value of the services rendered.
4. On White's part the contract is still executory because he has yet to pay Olsen the money for the clocks.
5. Yes. By watching the crew install the hot tub Girard has implied his agreement to go along with the contract.
6. Under quasi-contract rules, Adler will not have to pay for the wax job because it was unnecessary and because it was the result of negligence on the part of the E-Z Car Wash Company.
7. Contracts need not be long formal documents.
8. Hume's promise to take his brothers to the Super Bowl was a social arrangement, not a contract.
9. This was a bilateral contract. Therefore, the promises alone created a contract.
10. A contract made illegal by statutory laws is void.

Chapter 8
Legal Concepts

1. T	6. F	11. T
2. F	7. F	12. T
3. F	8. F	13. F
4. T	9. T	14. T
5. F	10. T	15. F

Language of the Law

1.	j	6.	e
2.	g	7.	f
3.	c	8.	o
4.	k	9.	l
5.	h	10.	i

Applying the Law

1. No. Marshall's statement is not an offer because there is no serious intent.
2. No. The terms here are too vague.
3. Ingalls should have made sure that Thomas agreed to pay a specific amount or a specific percentage of the expenses.
4. No. Kennedy did not know about the offer at the time that he discovered the watch.
5. Since Hatcher did not address the envelope properly, the acceptance is not effective until the letter is received.
6. Kubach changed the terms of the offer. Therefore, her response was not an acceptance. It was a counteroffer.
7. Ludwig's acceptance was implied.
8. The Postal Reorganization Act allows her to treat the towels as a gift.
9. The offeree can hold the offeror to a contract if the offeror set up silence as the condition of acceptance.
10. The $25 was consideration in the option contract. The offeror is under no obligation to return that consideration.

Chapter 9
Legal Concepts

1.	T	6.	T	11.	F
2.	T	7.	F	12.	T
3.	T	8.	T	13.	F
4.	F	9.	F	14.	F
5.	F	10.	T	15.	T

Language of the Law

1.	a	6.	i
2.	n	7.	b
3.	g	8.	k
4.	h	9.	m
5.	c	10.	o

Applying the Law

1. Yes. The subject of the contract had been destroyed before the contract was entered.
2. Hillier will fail in this request because a mistake as to the value of the subject matter of a contract is not grounds to rescind the contract.
3. Yes. Assent was destroyed by Williams' concealment of the hidden defect.
4. No. Unilateral mistake will not allow rescission.
5. Since the subject of the contract had been destroyed before the contract was entered, there could be no "meeting of the minds."
6. Chandler made a unilateral mistake as to the community's zoning laws. A unilateral mistake does not offer grounds for rescission of a contract. Chandler could have been protected by making the contract subject to obtaining all necessary permits to build a factory on the site.
7. Capriotti's statements are opinions. Such "sales puffery" is allowed.
8. Jamison's assent was destroyed by duress.
9. The misrepresentation will allow Hawkins to rescind the contract.
10. Calvarese knew that the statements made by the salesperson were false. Therefore, she had not relied on the statements in her purchase.

Chapter 10
Legal Concepts

1.	T	6.	T	11.	F
2.	F	7.	T	12.	T
3.	T	8.	F	13.	T
4.	T	9.	F	14.	F
5.	F	10.	T	15.	T

Language of the Law

1.	e	6.	c
2.	g	7.	a
3.	h	8.	j
4.	d	9.	b and i
5.	f	10.	k

Applying the Law

1. Yes. Since Urchek was a minor when the clothes were purchased, she can void the contract.

2. Yes. Since Boterus was a minor when the snowmobile was purchased, she can void the contract. This is true even though the snowmobile is damaged. Some states deduct something from the amount returned if the goods are damaged. Most, however, do not.

3. No. Cedric ratified the contract when the first installment payment was made.

4. No. Since Nadir had been declared incompetent by a court, all contracts that she entered were void.

5. No. Lopez purchased the laptop when she was a minor, and attempted to rescind the contract within a reasonable time after turning eighteen.

6. Despite the misrepresentation of age, most states will allow the minor to disaffirm or get out of the contract. Some states, however, have enacted statutes, which allow recovery against a minor when misrepresentation of age can be proved or when the minor is engaged in business. A number of states, for example, have statutes that deny disaffirmance if the minor has signed a written statement falsely asserting adult status. Without such a statute the minor will be allowed to get out of the contract despite her or his signature.

7. Burell had waited too long to rescind the contract. Two years is not a reasonable time.

8. The minor would have to pay for the coat, because it would be considered a necessary.

9. Contracts made by people who are intoxicated may be voidable if the intoxicated individual had lost the ability to comprehend the obligations entered under the terms of the agreement.

10. A contract made by a person who is mentally infirm or who suffers from a mental illness may be valid, if the person's infirmity or illness is not severe enough to rob that person of the ability to understand the nature, the purpose, and the effect of the agreement.

Chapter 11
Legal Concepts

1. T	6. F	11. T
2. T	7. T	12. T
3. T	8. F	13. F
4. T	9. F	14. F
5. F	10. F	15. F

Language of the Law

1. h	6. a
2. n	7. k
3. i	8. g
4. m	9. j
5. e	10. d

Applying the Law

1. No. The promise to pay itself is consideration.

2. No. The consideration of a stolen car in this situation is illegal. Consideration requires that the benefits and sacrifices promised be legal.

3. Promises not to sue are valid consideration.

4. No. Ken had the right to smoke. Giving up the right to smoke is a detriment legally, even if it is a benefit to his health.

5. No. The chief and his men already have the duty to fight the fire. A preexisting duty cannot be consideration in a new contract.

6. No. A promise to another to give something of value for a service rendered in the past is not valid consideration.

7. No genuine dispute exists as to the amount owed. Therefore, a partial payment in lieu of the full amount when

accepted by the creditor will not cancel the undisputed debt.

8. In this case, a genuine dispute as to the amount owed existed between Hartmann and Dr. Saltzer. Therefore, the doctor's acceptance of the lesser amount as full payment settled the dispute by accord and satisfaction.

9. Sanders cannot enforce a payment if the check is not sent because a promise to another to give something of value for a service rendered in the past is not valid consideration.

10. In this case, the church's promise to spend the amount donated on the installation of a new organ would be consideration.

Chapter 12
Legal Concepts

1. T	6. T	11. T
2. F	7. T	12. T
3. F	8. T	13. F
4. F	9. F	14. T
5. F	10. T	15. T

Language of the Law

1. d	6. g
2. f	7. e
3. k	8. a
4. l	9. j
5. i	10. m

Applying the Law

1. No. The law cannot honor an agreement to commit a crime.

2. Steele is charging Graf a rate of interest that is more than the amount allowed by law. Such usurious agreements are illegal.

3. Since a portion of the contract is illegal, the court will not enforce that portion of the contract.

4. The contract may be voidable based on the grounds that it is unconscionable due to the outrageous amount of consideration.

5. Dugan did not have the appropriate license. A pilot's license is designed to protect the public. Whenever a licensing requirement is designed to protect the public, the lack of a license will generally void the contract.

6. In agreements made as a part of the sale of a business, the buyer is allowed to restrict the future business activity of the seller if the restriction is reasonable as to geography, duration and the type of business prohibited. In this case, the 50 mile restriction and the ten year limit are probably too broad and, therefore, unreasonable.

7. When an employee has access to secret information, it is permissible for the employer to restrict the future employment of that employee as long as the restrictions are reasonable as to geography, duration, and the type of work. In this case, the five-year limit is reasonable.

8. The agreement made by Fairton is designed to obstruct justice. As such it is void.

9. The agreement between Hines and O'Neal is designed to suppress competition. Agreements made with the intent to suppress competition, fix prices, and the like, are void as illegal restraint of trade.

10. The agreement in this case was designed to interfere with a public service. As such, it was illegal and, therefore, void.

Chapter 13
Legal Concepts

1. F	6. F	11. T
2. F	7. T	12. F
3. F	8. F	13. T
4. F	9. T	14. T
5. T	10. F	15. F

Language of the Law

1. j
2. i
3. b
4. c
5. a
6. l
7. h
8. k
9. e
10. d

Applying the Law

1. No. Agreements made in consideration of marriage must be in writing to be enforceable. Prenuptial agreements are included in this category.
2. Yes. Contracts for the sale of goods under $500 need not be in writing to be enforceable.
3. No. Under the best-evidence rule, the courts will accept only the original of a writing and not a copy.
4. No. The Statute of Frauds requires a written memorandum as evidence of any promise by an executor or administrator to guarantee any debts owed by the estate. Gretto's promise was oral and, therefore, was not enforceable.
5. No. The Statute of Frauds requires that contracts for the sale of any interest in real property be in writing. The equal-dignities rule requires that in the appointment that must be in writing, the appointment must itself be in writing. Neither of these requirements was observed between Zelinski and Farm Realty Company.
6. No. All contracts that require more than one year from the date of making for performance will not be enforced unless evidenced by a written memorandum. O'Brien's employer was not bound by the oral agreement that covered a period of more than one year. She was employed on Thursday to commence working the following Monday for a period of one year. This, in total, was more than one year from the date of making.
7. Venturo would be permitted to make his mark (X) on the contract, witnessed by persons present who could later testify to his having accepted the contract offer. If he were not physically able to make his mark, another person could be selected to sign for him, with a statement attached giving the reasons for such signing.
8. Yes. A written memorandum is required in the sale of personal property valued at $500 or more. The Statute of Frauds does not specify how the memorandum should be made, as long as it is available as evidence in proving the intentions of the parties. The two letters, when brought together, would contain the necessary information and the signatures required to act as a written memorandum.
9. No. Agreements and promises that guarantee the debts or guarantee against the wrongdoings of another must be in writing. Aparicio offered his guarantee to the seller in a telephone conversation. The promise was not in writing, as required by the Statute of Frauds. Aparicio's obligations, then, are in no way legally enforceable - only a moral obligation exists.
10. No. The parol evidence rule states that when an agreement is reduced to written form, only those terms and conditions contained in the written document will be enforceable. Jeness's agreement failed to mention the guarantee made orally to her by the seller's representative.

Chapter 14
Legal Concepts

1. F
2. F
3. F
4. T
5. T
6. F
7. T
8. T
9. T
10. T
11. F
12. T
13. F
14. F
15. T

Language of the Law

1. i
2. g
3. b
4. k
5. f
6. h
7. c
8. d
9. j
10. n

Applying the Law

1. No. Consideration is not required in the creation of an assignment, but when there is no consideration the assignor may repudiate the assignment at any time prior to its execution.

2. Yes. As a measure of protection, the assignee should give notice of the assignment to the obligor. This notice is an obligation of the assignee, not the assignor. If notice is not given, it would be normal practice for the obligor to render performance to the original contracting party.

3. No. To have a novation, the original parties to a contract (the assignor and the obligor) must agree to releasing the assignor. Morris, the obligor in this case, did not agree to the change.

4. Yes. Contracts related to professional services may not be assigned without the express permission of the obligor. Dr. Gravers exceeded his rights in attempting to assign the O'Leary case to Dr. Harrison. Physicians now usually secure this permission from a patient whom they accept for long-term treatment, as in the case presented here.

5. Yes. Rawlins is an insurance beneficiary, recognized as an intended beneficiary. There is no need for the beneficiary's rights to be supported by consideration tendered by the beneficiary. Consideration supporting the insurer's obligation was made in the form of premiums paid by Sung.

6. No. Continental Paint Company was an incidental beneficiary to the agreement between Bay Bridge Authority and Salakas. An incidental beneficiary, in contrast to an intended beneficiary, has no legal grounds for enforcing the contract made by those in privity of contract.

7. No. The equal-dignities rule requires that an assignment be in writing if the agreement assigned required a writing. The Statute of Frauds requires that Jenkins's agreement with Harcourt be in writing. Likewise, Jenkins's assignment to Campbell must also be in writing in order to be enforceable.

8. No. Parties to a contract may include a condition that will not allow its assignment.

9. Yes. With exceptions in some states, intended beneficiaries can enforce the contract made by those in privity of contract. Myette's daughter was a donee beneficiary.

10. No. A party may not delegate duties that are of a personal nature. Wintersteen was chosen for her artistic talent; therefore, Carter could expect to have the work done by her.

Chapter 15
Legal Concepts

1.	T	6.	F	11.	F
2.	F	7.	F	12.	T
3.	F	8.	T	13.	T
4.	T	9.	F	14.	T
5.	F	10.	T	15.	F

Language of the Law

1.	k	6.	i
2.	c	7.	m
3.	l	8.	j
4.	a	9.	n
5.	d	10.	h

Applying the Law

1. No. Impossibility of performance terminates and discharges personal-service contracts when impossibility is related to physical impairment, illness, injury, and the like, over which a party has no control. Raymond's broken fingers could not be attributed to her own negligence or intentional act. The condition could not have been prevented from occurring; therefore she would be

discharged from performing the otherwise enforceable agreement with the tenor.

2. Yes. Overdue accounts may be avoided by a debtor by pleading the statute of limitations as a defense. Damico had neither made any payment nor otherwise reaffirmed his bill for a period longer than that covered by the statute of limitations, which is four years for the sale of goods.

3. No. Contracts may be discharged when the subject matter is contrary to either existing or subsequently adopted laws or regulations. The Consumer Product Safety Commission (CPSC) had authority to regulate the use of the questionable materials if used in the manufacture of infants' garments. The contract may not, then, be enforced by either Softknit Industries or Tender Years.

4. When a party has experienced an injury to legal rights but has no proof of damages, a court will usually award nominal damages: six cents or one dollar in many courts today.

5. No. Anticipatory breach permits the beginning of an action for damages at the time of the breach. There is no requirement that the injured party must wait for the date of performance in order to institute action.

6. No. One who breaches a contract through abandonment has no right to demand payment for labor and materials used up to the time of abandonment. Lukens did abandon performance on Marinelli's computer, giving Marinelli the right to regain possession of the computer without the obligation to reward Lukens for the time spent in testing the computer.

7. No. Specific performance will not be granted as a relief to one injured through nonperformance of a personal-service contract. A court of equity would not demand performance by the Soul Singers. An equity court could, however, grant a restraining injunction that would prohibit the group from performing anywhere else at the time they had contracted to perform for Lacey's Lounge. Lacey's Lounge might also institute an action in a court of law for damages.

8. Yes. Dr. Spires has breached the agreement with Chemical Research. Through an action in equity, Chemical Research may seek a restraining injunction against its former employee, prohibiting Spires from continuing with the position obtained with Chemical Research's competitor.

9. No. There had been substantial performance. Failure to mow only a few square feet as part of a large area would not amount to a breach of the mowing contract. However, the landscape gardener is not excused for even that small part that was not done. Buzby may deduct from the gardener's payment an amount equivalent to the work that was not finished.

10. No. Only when time is of the essence may a party repudiate an obligation for reason of tardy performance and completion. Although April 15 had been agreed to as the completion date, that specific date was not essential to the real intent or performance of the contract.

Chapter 16
Legal Concepts

1.	T	6.	F	11.	T
2.	F	7.	T	12.	F
3.	T	8.	T	13.	T
4.	T	9.	T	14.	F
5.	F	10.	F	15.	T

Language of the Law

1.	d	6.	g
2.	c	7.	l
3.	f	8.	k
4.	j	9.	m
5.	a	10.	e

1. Yes. As long as a purchase price is under $500, an oral contract for the sale of goods is enforceable.
2. No. An agreement modifying a contract for the sale of goods needs no consideration to be binding.
3. No. Future goods are things not yet acquired for use, such as fish in the sea, animals in their wild state, and minerals not yet mined. When the fish were in the ocean, they were future goods. Once caught and landed by the fleet, they were converted to goods available for immediate sale.
4. No. Under the UCC, a contract for goods that are to be specially manufactured for the buyer and are not suitable for sale to others in the ordinary course of the seller's business need not be in writing if the seller has made either a substantial beginning in manufacturing the goods or has made commitments to buy materials necessary to manufacture the goods.
5. No. In this sales agreement the purchase price exceeded $500. Without a written agreement signed by Stewart, Best's Cycle Shop would be powerless to enforce Stewart's oral promise unless Stewart were to admit in court that an oral agreement took place.
6. The UCC, which has been adopted by all three states, would govern the transaction because it involves a contract for the sale of goods.
7. No. Future goods were involved. It is not possible to have a sale of goods not yet in existence. This agreement was a contract for sale.
8. No. The car dealer made a firm offer, which occurs when a merchant promises in writing to hold open an offer for the sale of goods. A firm offer requires no consideration and must be held open for one week for Webster to accept if he wishes.

9. Yes. In a sale with reserve, the auctioneer may withdraw the goods at any time before announcing the completion of the sale.
10. No. The employment contract was not governed by the UCC because it was not a contract for the sale of goods. Rather, it was a contract for services, which is governed by the common law of contracts.

Chapter 17
Legal Concepts

1.	T	6.	F	11.	T
2.	T	7.	F	12.	F
3.	F	8.	T	13.	F
4.	T	9.	T	14.	T
5.	T	10.	T	15.	T

Language of the Law

1.	d	6.	e
2.	j	7.	n
3.	c	8.	g
4.	f	9.	l
5.	o	10.	i

Applying the Law

1. No. When the goods are held by a bailee to be delivered without being moved, the risk of loss passes to the buyer when he or she receives a document of title describing the goods. Eastern Milling assumed the risk of loss when it received the elevator receipt for the 150,000 bushels of corn.
2. Yes. This was a sale on approval, because the TV was primarily for the buyer's use. In a sale on approval, the risk of loss remains with the seller until the buyer has accepted the goods.
3. No. When terms of shipment do not specify shipping point or destination, it is assumed to be f.o.b. for the place of shipment. Adding the term c.o.d. instructs the carrier to retain possession until the carrier has collected the cost of the goods.

4. Because Hamlin was to deliver the piano, the risk of loss was with Hamlin during transit. It would pass to Jefferson only when delivery was complete.

5. Yes. Hopkins had promised to contact Winter if he decided not to buy the machine. No contact was made during the two weeks agreed upon. Hopkins therefore implied that he had decided to buy the machine after the passing of the "trial on approval" period of two weeks.

6. No. The museum received valid title from Knapp, who had only a voidable title. Rigby could have recovered the mirror from Knapp prior to its sale to the museum. Following the sale of the mirror to the museum, however, Rigby no longer had title rights in her former property.

7. Warne must suffer the loss because the tractor had been tendered to him. When the contract calls for the buyer to pick up the goods and the seller is not a merchant, the risk of loss passes to the buyer when the seller tenders the goods to the buyer.

8. No. When a merchant sells goods in the ordinary course of business to a third party who has no knowledge of the real owner's rights, the third party receives good title to them. Lee gave the seller rightful possession of the watch. Hill made an innocent purchase for value, with no way of knowing that the watch had already been sold. Lee may not recover the watch from Hill, but may sue the store for the value of the watch.

9. No. Title to stolen goods never passes, even though the goods have passed through several innocent owners' hands. Esposito did buy the car from someone whose business it was to sell cars. The real owner, however, was not the person who gave the car to Sanders Used-Car Sales. In the entire chain of sales up to Esposito, no one ever had rightful possession. Esposito, however, could claim damages from Sanders.

10. Yes. Risk of loss passed as the shipping point, Moline, Illinois. When the goods are sent f.o.b. the place of shipment, the risk of loss passes at the point of origin. Delivery to the carrier by the seller and acceptance by the carrier complete the transfer of both title and risk of loss to Ward, who would have a cause of action against the carrier for the loss.

Chapter 18
Legal Concepts

1.	T	6.	F	11.	F
2.	F	7.	F	12.	F
3.	T	8.	T	13.	F
4.	T	9.	T	14.	T
5.	T	10.	T	15.	T

Language of the Law

1.	d	6.	g
2.	m	7.	i
3.	n	8.	l
4.	k	9.	o
5.	c	10.	j

Applying the Law

1. No. Merchant buyers have a duty after the rejection of goods in their possession to follow any reasonable instructions received from the seller with respect to the goods. If there are no instructions, merchant buyers must make reasonable efforts to sell perishable goods.

2. Yes. Under the UCC, when either party repudiates the contract before the time for performance, the injured party may take action immediately if it would be unjust or would cause a material inconvenience to wait longer. This early action is known as anticipatory repudiation.

3. Yes. When defective or nonconforming goods are delivered, the buyer may accept any commercial unit or units and reject the rest. The set of furniture would be

considered a commercial unit, which Style Rite could reject.

4. Yes. Because the antique mirror was unique and not readily available on the open market, Rousette could bring an action in equity for specific performance of the contract. A decree of specific performance, if granted by the court, would require the seller to deliver the antique mirror to the buyer.

5. No. The statute of limitations had run out. Under the UCC, an action for breach of contract must be commenced within four years after the date of the breach.

6. Davis could ask the court to find the contract unconscionable. The salesperson's knowledge of Davis's financial situation together with a price that was unreasonably high might cause the court to hold this contract unconscionable.

7. No. When a contract requires payment before inspection, as when goods are shipped c.o.d., the buyer must pay for them first, even if they turn out to be defective when they are inspected. Payment by the buyer before inspecting the goods does not constitute an acceptance of them.

8. Yes. Tender of payment may be made by any means or in any manner that is commonly used in the ordinary course of business, but the seller may demand payment in legal tender if he or she gives the buyer reasonable time to obtain it. Valley Supply must give Vaughn Corporation a reasonable time to obtain cash.

9. No. Although the buyer is obligated to accept and pay for the goods after a contract for sale has been made, this obligation is conditioned upon the seller making tender of delivery. Failure of the seller to do this is an excuse for the buyer not to perform his or her part of the bargain. Since Meehan did not make tender

of delivery of the goods, he was not in a position to bring suit because he had not tested Katz's ability or willingness to perform.

10. Yes. Lenz could revoke her acceptance. A revocation is allowable when the buyer accepts goods on the assumption that their nonconformity will be corrected by the seller and the seller does not make the correction.

Chapter 19
Legal Concepts

1. T	6. F	11. T
2. T	7. F	12. F
3. F	8. T	13. T
4. T	9. T	14. T
5. T	10. F	15. F

Language of the Law

1. f	6. c	
2. d	7. a	
3. h	8. j	
4. g	9. m	
5. n	10. l	

Applying the Law

1. Yes. Under the doctrine of strict liability, the manufacturer's and seller's liability for selling unreasonably dangerous goods extends to anyone who may be injured by the product.

2. When a sale is made by presentation of sample, there is an express warranty that goods delivered will be like the samples. In this case, the books did not meet the high quality of the sample. Thus, there was a breach of the seller's express warranty.

3. Yes. Whenever a seller of goods makes an affirmation of fact about the goods to the buyer, an express warranty is created. The seller warrants that the goods will live up to the affirmation. The statement by Enos that the painting was an original of a well-known artist created an express

warranty. This warranty was breached when the painting turned out to be a copy.

4. No. The buyer in this case did not rely on the seller's skill and judgment to select the dish. The buyer asked for no assistance in seeking the dish best suited to a particular location.

5. No. In many states today, product liability extends even to remote parties. Originally it extended to the buyer, then to family and guests, and now to almost anyone who may be injured as a result of defective design, manufacture, or assembly.

6. Yes. Any description of the goods that is made part of the basis of the bargain creates an express warranty that the goods will be as described.

7. No. To recover damages for breach of warranty, a buyer of defective goods must notify the seller within a reasonable time after discovering the defect.

8. Yes. Kelley had an opportunity to examine the mower, but the trial was limited to an operation that did not provide an opportunity to determine whether the mower would operate properly under the conditions for which it was sold. Thus, the seller breached the implied warranty of fitness for a particular purpose. In addition, the seller breached the express warranty that the machine was sharp and would do a good job on the lawn. There was also a breach of the implied warranty of merchantability, since the mower was not fit for the ordinary purposes for which mowers are used.

9. Yes. In this case, the buyer has a right to receive a micrometer fit for the use for which it was sold. There was a breach of the implied warranty of merchantability and, possibly, of fitness for a particular purpose.

10. No. Distribution of human blood is considered a service; therefore, the law of warranties does not apply.

Chapter 20
Legal Concepts

1.	T	6.	F	11.	F
2.	F	7.	T	12.	T
3.	F	8.	F	13.	F
4.	T	9.	T	14.	F
5.	T	10.	F	15.	F

Language of the Law

1.	b	6.	k
2.	j	7.	d
3.	m	8.	n
4.	g	9.	l
5.	h	10.	i

Applying the Law

1. Yes. Under the FTC Mail Order Rule, sellers must either ship an order within thirty days or send the consumer notice of a delay in shipment and give the consumer the option of agreeing to the delay or canceling the order and receiving a prompt refund.

2. Yes. Under the Equal Credit Opportunity Act, creditors must consider public assistance income in exactly the same way they consider other income.

3. No. For the Fair Credit Billing Act to apply, the initial transaction must have taken place in the consumer's state or within 100 miles of the consumer's mailing address.

4. Yes. Javeo was subjected to bait-and-switch advertising, which is an unfair and deceptive act. The FTC rule states, "No advertisement containing an offer to sell a product shall be made when the offer is not a bona fide effort to sell the advertised product."

5. Yes. Blair violated the Federal Odometer Law. A car owner, in this situation, must attach to the left-door frame of the car a written notice showing the true mileage before the repair or replacement of the odometer and the date that the odometer was set back to zero.

6. No. Carlucci's liability for the unauthorized use of his credit card was limited to the first $50 of the total charges.
7. Yes. Romano was protected by the regulation governing a cooling-off period for sales of consumer goods or services with the purchase price of $25 or more in which the seller solicits the sale and the agreement is made at a place other than the seller's place of business. He could cancel the transaction at any time prior to midnight of the third business day after the date of the transaction. The supplier must refund Romano's $300 down payment within ten business days after receiving the notice of cancellation.
8. Ley can order a credit report from Equifax, TransUnion, or Experian over the Internet or by telephone.
9. No. The unsolicited distribution of credit cards to people who have not applied for them is prohibited. In order to impose liability of up to $50, the issuer of the card must show that the credit card was requested by the cardholder.
10. Defano can best stop receiving the unwanted calls by placing her telephone number on the Do Not Call Registry.

Chapter 21
Legal Concepts

1.	F	6.	F	11.	T
2.	F	7.	F	12.	T
3.	T	8.	T	13.	F
4.	F	9.	T	14.	T
5.	F	10.	F	15.	T

Language of the Law

1.	n	6.	b
2.	d	7.	k
3.	f	8.	m
4.	a	9.	j
5.	i	10.	l

Applying the Law
1. Yes. Gifts given *in causa mortis* must be returned if the donor so desires if death does not come to the donor or if the donor dies from causes other than those feared.
2. No. Currently, a child's unearned income above $1,700 is taxable at the parent's top tax rate. This was less than that amount.
3. No. To be eligible for registration under the Federal Trademark Act of 1946, goods or services must be sold or used in more than one state or in this and a foreign country.
4. No. One who finds property of another and takes possession of it becomes a bailee. This is a bailment for the sole benefit of the bailor. The finder must make an effort to locate the owner.
5. Yes. The pocketbook is considered to have been *misplaced,* not *lost.* It is reasonable to suppose that the owner will remember leaving it there and return for it. For this reason, the finder may not keep the article in his or her possession but must leave it with the manager to hold for the owner.
6. No. A thief acquires no title to stolen goods, and, therefore, cannot convey good title to anyone. Cruz has no title to the tools. His recourse is against LaRue for breach of warranty of title.
7. No. To be legally protected, a patent item must be marked with the word *patent* followed by the patent number.
8. No. Noncommercial recording of material broadcast over the public airwaves that is intended for home use only is a fair use of copyrighted works and does not constitute copyright infringement.
9. No. The fair-use doctrine provides that copyrighted material may be reproduced without permission if the use of the material is reasonable and not harmful to the rights of the copyright owner.

10. Kupid Kandy Kompany can claim that a common law trademark has been established by usage because of the quality and duration of their lollipops. "Kupid" developed a secondary meaning – not merely identification of the product but rather identification of its producer.

Chapter 22
Legal Concepts

1. T	6. F	11. F
2. F	7. F	12. T
3. T	8. T	13. T
4. T	9. T	14. F
5. F	10. T	15. T

Language of the Law

1. i	6. o
2. l	7. m
3. k	8. c
4. e	9. f
5. n	10. g

Applying the Law

1. No. The law has no requirements for returning items that are left at security checkpoints. In addition, those who attempt to bring banned items through airport checkpoints are subject to civil penalties of up to $1,100 per violation as well as criminal penalties.
2. The borrowing of the flour was a mutuum rather than a bailment because the parties did not intend that the identical particles of flour that were borrowed would be returned.
3. No. A common carrier is excused of liability as an insurer of goods shipped when damage results from an act of God.
4. Yes. Mueller was a bailee in a bailment for the sole benefit of the bailee. He was required to exercise great care. He had been negligent in placing the binoculars on a seat in a public place without watching them and was, therefore, liable for damages for this loss.
5. No. Anderson locked the doors to the garage after the car had been placed inside. This was a bailment for the sole benefit of the bailor, and Anderson was obligated to exercise slight care. It would seem that locking the door was as much care as he could have given under the circumstances. He was not an insurer.
6. Yes. Harris exceeded his authority in the use of the boat when he went beyond the island. When one exceeds the permitted use of another's property, he or she becomes liable for any resulting losses from any cause. Harris will be required to pay for the boat regardless of his defense that he had not been negligent.
7. No. A warehouser's lien is a possessory one. The lien was lost when Dexter turned the goods over to McKay.
8. Yes. The carrier is an insurer of luggage that was accepted for shipment in the luggage area of the plane, however, the maximum liability of the airline is $3,000 per passenger.
9. No. Airline passengers who are bumped may be entitled to compensation. If the airline can arrange alternate transportation that is scheduled to arrive at the passenger's destination within one hour of the original arrival time, there is no compensation. However, if the alternate flight gets to the destination between one and two hours late, the passenger is entitled to a cash payment equal to the price of one fare up to $200. This amount is doubled if the passenger is more than two hours late.
10. No. A common carrier has a lien on all goods shipped for the shipping charges due. The carrier has the right to sell the goods at public sale to obtain the amount due.

Chapter 23
Legal Concepts

1. F	6. T	11. F
2. T	7. F	12. F
3. T	8. F	13. T
4. F	9. F	14. T
5. F	10. T	15. T

Language of the Law

1. i	6. d
2. o	7. m
3. e	8. b
4. j	9. h
5. k	10. f

Applying the Law

1. Yes. Except for when it is used for landing and taking off, the navigable airspace is the space above 1,000 feet over populated areas and above 500 feet over water and unpopulated areas.
2. No. A life estate lasts for the duration of the owner's life. LaPlant's daughter could live at Stillwater Farm until the death of her mother, but for no longer.
3. No. Title passed to Andrew at the moment of his father's death. The record of the probate court establishes Andrew's title to the property.
4. No. Once an easement is created, it runs with the land. Future owners have the right to use the easement unless they surrender their right by deed or by not using the easement for a long period of time.
5. No. Because California is a community property jurisdiction, the farmhouse belongs to both spouses equally.
6. Yes. Landowners may draw only that supply of water reasonably required to satisfy their needs. Other property owners damaged by unreasonable use may seek an injunction against such use in a court of equity.
7. Yes. Growing things that have been planted with the intention of their remaining in the ground and recycling their growth each year are the fruits of nature. Such things are real property. Hawthorne, after buying the property, had title to all the real property, including the plantings being removed by the former owner. Starrett was obliged to discontinue removing the bulbs and plants. Hawthorne could hold her liable for damage already
8. Yes. Owners of property through which a flowing stream passes have riparian rights. Riparian rights include equal rights to the use of the water passing by or through their property.
9. No. The court would rule that Rheinhold was prevented from the full and quiet enjoyment of his property and had the right to cut off the limbs and roots of the tree.
10. No. A general warranty deed is the most desirable form of deed because it warrants that title is good.

Chapter 24
Legal Concepts

1. T	6. F	11. F
2. F	7. F	12. F
3. F	8. T	13. T
4. T	9. T	14. T
5. F	10. T	15. F

Language of the Law

1. c	6. f
2. a	7. o
3. i	8. h
4. l	9. m
5. k	10. b

Applying the Law

1. No. The landlord is responsible for injuries to others caused by a defect in any common area.
2. No. Tenants are responsible, in most cases, for injuries caused by defects in the portion of the premises over which they have control.

3. Yes. When a tenant is deprived of something of a substantial nature that is called for under the tenant's lease (the heat in this case), the situation is called a constructive eviction. The tenant is justified in abandoning the premises without paying rent when such a situation occurs.

4. Yes. The death of a tenant who holds a periodic tenancy does not terminate the tenancy. Rather, the interest of the tenant passes to the personal representative of the deceased's estate.

5. No. Under a periodic tenancy, unless the landlord or the tenant gives advance notice of an intention to terminate the lease, it will be automatically renewed at the end of each period for the same term.

6. No. A tenant is not responsible for repairs resulting from normal wear and tear. Normal wear and tear includes the gradual depreciation of an apartment's decoration. A security deposit may not be kept for redecorating an apartment or a house for succeeding tenants.

7. Yes. A landlord as no special right to enter rented premises. If the landlord reserves the right of inspection in a lease, the inspection must be made at reasonable hours and in the presence of the tenant.

8. No. Sorkora was a lodger. She had the use of the property without actual or exclusive possession of it. She was a type of licensee, with a mere right to use the property. The landlord retained control of the premises and was responsible for its care and upkeep.

9. No. A tenancy at sufferance arises when a tenant wrongfully remains in possession of the premises after his or her tenancy has expired. Such a tenant is a wrongdoer, having no estate or other interest in the property.

10. Yes. O'Brian had what is known as a tenancy at will. Most states have statutes requiring the lessor to give at least thirty days' written notice of eviction in such tenancies. O'Brian received no advance notice and would be within his rights in remaining for another month.

Chapter 25
Legal Concepts

1. F	6. F	11. F
2. T	7. F	12. F
3. F	8. T	13. T
4. F	9. F	14. T
5. T	10. T	15. F

Language of the Law

1. i	6. l
2. d	7. a
3. f	8. e
4. c	9. b
5. n	10. j

Applying the Law

1. Yes. A surviving spouse who does not like the provisions of a deceased spouse's will may waive the will and take an amount set by state statute.

2. A person must have reached the age of eighteen to be able to make a valid will. Since Becket's will was not allowed, Becket's estate passed to his parents under the law of intestacy.

3. No. Stepchildren do not inherit from a stepparent who dies intestate. The law of wills allows people to leave their estates to anyone they wish with the exception that no one can disinherit a surviving spouse.

4. Yes. Although the will was invalid because it had only one witness, a properly executed codicil has the effect of republishing a will. A codicil breathes new life into a will. Thus the improperly executed will was made valid by the properly signed and witnessed codicil.

5. The word *heirs* includes all persons of the same bloodline. Children are heirs, but all heirs are not the testator's children.

6. No. The person whose name was newly inserted in the will would not inherit from Howell's estate because the addition to the will was not executed properly. To be valid, the will would have had to be re-signed by Howell, and witnesses would have had to attest and subscribe again to her signature. In addition, the person whose name was blanked out would not inherit because Howell canceled that person's name with the intent to do so.

7. No. Witnesses must sign in the presence of the testator and, in some states, in each others' presence.

8. The Uniform Simultaneous Death Act will govern the settlement of their estates. The separately-owned property of each person will pass as if he or she had survived the other. Singh's property will pass to her two children; DeFazio's property will pass to his child.

9. In states that still respect the holographic will, Elizabeth Thorton's writing will serve as her will. The will is entirely in the handwriting of the testator and was found among the deceased's personal and valuable papers, where she would naturally have placed a will. Holographic wills do not have to be witnessed and require none of the usual formalities of a regular will. However, many states do not recognize a holographic will.

10. Yes. The signature of a testator is valid even when indicated by an *X*. It must be witnessed by persons who can attest to Chi's placing the *X* where the signature would ordinarily appear.

Chapter 26
Legal Concepts

1.	F	6.	T	11.	T
2.	T	7.	F	12.	F
3.	T	8.	T	13.	F
4.	F	9.	T	14.	T
5.	F	10.	T	15.	F

Language of the Law

1.	m	6.	b
2.	a	7.	h
3.	f	8.	l
4.	n	9.	k
5.	g	10.	d

Applying the Law

1. No. A demand note is payable whenever the payee demands payment.

2. No. A bearer is a person who is in possession of a negotiable instrument that is payable to bearer or to cash or indorsed in blank.

3. For Giron to be a holder, the check would have had to be indorsed by Luciano P. Mancuso.

4. No. A negotiation is the transfer of an instrument in such a way that the transferee (Giron) becomes a holder. Since the check was not issued or indorsed to Giron or to bearer or in blank, Giron was not a holder; thus, the instrument was not negotiated.

5. The check was order paper because it read "pay to the order of," and was not indorsed by the payee, Mancuso.

6. Yes. It is a draft, since it is an order to Leon Sloboda by the drawer, Monte Miranda, to pay money to the order of Xavier Monaco.

7. No. A negotiable instrument must be payable in a fixed amount of money. Money is defined as a medium of exchange adopted by a domestic or foreign government and need not be money of the United States.

8. No. Silver is not money; therefore, the instrument was not negotiable.

9. Yes. It is negotiable because it contains a promise to pay: "I promise to pay to the order of. . . ." The statement that it was given for merchandise is not a condition.

10. Yes. For an instrument to be negotiable it must contain an unconditional promise or order to pay a fixed amount of money on

demand or at a definite time. The note must be payable independent of the occurrence of any event. In this case, the payment was to be made when Jeanne Streeter was to attain her majority, an event that might or might not take place. In addition, the instrument was not a promise or order to pay.

Chapter 27
Legal Concepts

1. F	6. T	11. F
2. T	7. F	12. T
3. T	8. T	13. F
4. T	9. T	14. F
5. T	10. T	15. T

Language of the Law

1. n	6. m
2. d	7. h
3. b	8. l
4. g	9. a
5. f	10. e

Applying the Law

1. No. The transfer was an assignment rather than a negotiation because Brown, the payee, did not indorse the check.
2. Yes. The transfer was an assignment because David, the payee, indorsed the check in blank, turning it into bearer paper.
3. Yes. Because the check became bearer paper when David indorsed it in blank, it could be further negotiated by delivery alone without an indorsement by Earnest.
4. If David had indorsed the check with a special indorsement, that is, "pay to Frank (signed) David," Frank would have had to indorse the instrument to negotiate it.
5. (a) No because the check was not indorsed by Brown. A holder is a person who is in possession of an instrument that is issued or indorsed to that person, to that person's order, to bearer, or in

blank. (b) Yes, because the check was indorsed by Earnest. (c) Yes, because the check was indorsed in blank, making it bearer paper.
6. Yes. When an instrument is indorsed in blank, it becomes payable to bearer; therefore, the stranger who found the check was a holder of bearer paper. Bearer paper may be negotiated by delivery alone.
7. When a check is indorsed "for deposit only," the amount of the instrument will be credited to the indorser's account before it is negotiated further. This indorsement provides protection in the event that the check is stolen.
8. Yes. Any indorser who does not limit his or her obligation by means of a qualified indorsement is required to pay any subsequent holder of the check the face amount of the instrument if given proper notice.
9. Yes. By indorsing the note, Burns gave the implied warranty that the note was genuine and that it was all that it purported to be. The "maker" of the note (Gore) has no liability inasmuch as the Gore signature was a forgery. Burns remains responsible for loss suffered by Gossett or any subsequent holder.
10. No. The qualified indorsement would relieve Raughley of liability only if there were not sufficient money for payment of the instrument. The qualified indorsement does not avoid the indorser's liability for certain warranties that are implied by law, such as that the instrument has not been materially altered.

Chapter 28
Legal Concepts

1. T	6. F	11. T
2. T	7. T	12. T
3. T	8. F	13. T
4. F	9. T	14. F
5. F	10. F	15. F

Language of the Law

1.	d	6.	h
2.	g	7.	i or j
3.	n	8.	e
4.	f	9.	b
5.	k	10.	m

Applying the Law

1. No. To be a holder in due course, the person in possession of the instrument must first be a holder. The bank was not a holder because the check was not issued or indorsed to Schultz, to bearer or in blank.
2. No. A person must give value for an instrument in order to qualify as a holder in due course.
3. Yes. A holder who receives an instrument from a holder in due course acquires the rights of the holder in due course even though he or she does not qualify as a holder in due course. Watson was a holder in due course because he gave value for the instrument.
4. To be a holder in due course, a holder must not have notice that an instrument is overdue. A check is overdue ninety days after its date. The grocery store was not a holder in due course because the date on the check, which was four months old, gave the store notice that the check was overdue.
5. No. Minority is a real defense that is good even against a holder in due course. A minor who signs a note may refuse to pay as promised. The dealer, however, must respect the implied warranty that all prior parties had the capacity to contract and would be liable to the bank for the loss of $1,000 on the note.
6. No. Forgery or fraud through trickery is a real defense that is good against all holders. Creedon, however, who negotiated the note by indorsement, would be liable to the holder on the indorser's warranties that she had good

title to the note, that it was genuine in all respects, and that it would be honored when presented for acceptance and for payment.
7. No. Nondelivery of a completed instrument is a personal defense and may be used against Pappas but not against the bank, which is a holder in due course.
8. Yes. When a seller of consumer products has an arrangement with a financial institution to finance the seller's customer's purchases, the financial institution is subject to the customer's personal defenses and loses its holder-in-due-course protection.
9. No. Any person who negligently contributes to a material alteration of an instrument may not exercise the defense of alteration against a holder in due course, a drawee, or another payor who pays the instrument in good faith.
10. It is possible for a purchaser to become a holder in due course of an instrument that has been altered, if he or she bought it in good faith. The purchaser, however, has a duty to investigate when irregularity is sufficient to excite suspicion. In this case, the alteration was apparent on the face of the note; it was not regular on its face, and the taker had notice of the irregularity as an indication that something was wrong.

Chapter 29
Legal Concepts

1.	F	6.	F	11.	F
2.	T	7.	T	12.	T
3.	T	8.	T	13.	T
4.	T	9.	T	14.	T
5.	F	10.	F	15.	F

Language of the Law

1.	k	6.	a
2.	j	7.	f
3.	e	8.	c
4.	n	9.	o
5.	i	10.	l

Applying the Law

1. No. Under the Check 21 Act, customers have the right to a copy of the substitute check but not the return of the original canceled check.

2. No. Spencer will be responsible for paying $500 of the loss. A bank customer has two business days to report the loss or theft of a debit card to be responsible for paying only $50 of the loss. If notice is delayed beyond that time, customers' liability increases to $500 and becomes unlimited when notice is not given within 60 days.

3. Yes. A bank may pay or certify checks for ten days after the date of death of the drawer, even if it has notice of death.

4. No. A drawee bank has no liability to the holder of a check unless the check is certified.

5. Yes. If a bank fails to honor a check because of a mistake on the bank's part, the bank is liable to the customer for any actual damages the customer suffers.

6. Yes. The bank was liable to Amato because it paid a check on which her signature had been forged; a forgery has no effect as a signature. The burden of knowing the signatures of all its depositors is placed on the bank. The bank alone is responsible for determining whether the signature of the drawer, its customer, is a forgery. Only in the event of the drawer's contributory negligence, such as signing checks with a mechanical writer and not exercising reasonable care to prevent unauthorized persons from making use of the machine, would the depositor be barred from objecting to the payment of the check by the bank.

7. Richards, as drawer of the check, committed attempted larceny or larceny, but he would be granted a specific number of days in which to make the check good without fear of prosecution.

8. No. Horne will be entitled to withdraw $100 on Thursday and the balance on Friday. The banking day of deposit in this case is Wednesday because Horne made the deposit after the bank's cut-off hour for Tuesday.

9. No. A bank us under no obligation to a customer to pay a stale check (one that is over six months old). A bank may, however, honor a stale check without liability to its customer if it acts in good faith.

10. No. An oral stop-payment order is binding upon the bank for fourteen calendar days only, unless confirmed in handwriting within that period.

Chapter 30
Legal Concepts

1. T	6. F	11. F
2. T	7. T	12. F
3. F	8. T	13. T
4. F	9. F	14. T
5. T	10. T	15. F

Language of the Law

1. e	6. m
2. b	7. h
3. g	8. i
4. f	9. o
5. d	10. k

Applying the Law

1. Yes. A life insurance policy will remain valid and enforceable even if the insurable interest terminates.

2. Ovando could collect the insurance. An insurable interest in property must exist when the insurance contract is entered into and when the loss occurs.

3. No. Most policies provide that beneficiaries cannot recover for a death caused by suicide if the death takes place within two years after the policy was taken out.

4. The clause that allowed Anthony Darnell to collect $200,000 is known as a double indemnity clause. Such a clause provides that if the insured dies from accidental causes, the insurer will pay the beneficiary double the amount of the policy.

5. No. An insurer's liability under a fire policy usually covers losses other than those directly attributed to fire. Lightning damage, even if there is no resultant fire, is usually one of these losses.

6. Rosen would need property damage liability insurance to cover him for the damage to Kaplan's property. Such insurance provides protection when other people bring claims or lawsuits against the insured for damaging property such as a car, a fence, or a tree. The person bringing the claim or the suit (Kaplan in this case) must prove that the driver of the motor vehicle was at fault.

7. Quin and Clifford should arrange for a binder. A binder will provide temporary coverage until the policy is formally accepted.

8. Yes. If an insured party answers questions on an insurance application with false answers or misrepresentations that materially affect the risk undertaken by the insurer, the contract is voidable by the insurer.

9. Yes. Under the doctrine of estoppel, when an insurer has granted the insured a special dispensation, the insurer cannot deny that dispensation when the chance to cancel or deny liability does arise.

10. No. A warranty is an insured's promise to abide by restrictions specially written into a policy. If an insured breaches the warranty, the insurer can cancel the contract or refuse to pay benefits if the insured suffers a loss.

Chapter 31
Legal Concepts

1.	T	6.	F	11.	F
2.	F	7.	F	12.	T
3.	F	8.	T	13.	T
4.	T	9.	F	14.	F
5.	T	10.	T	15.	T

Language of the Law

1.	g	6.	n
2.	a	7.	b
3.	f	8.	c
4.	h	9.	k
5.	d	10.	i

Applying the Law

1. No. If property must be sold to satisfy a secured debt and the sale of the property does not satisfy the whole debt, the debtor still owes the balance.

2. Yes. Variable-rate mortgage agreements must include a maximum rate that cannot be exceeded.

3. No. Under a deed of trust, if the debtor defaults, the trustee can sell the property without going to court.

4. No. A failure to record a first mortgage does not remove the obligation of the mortgagor to the mortgagee.

5. No. Under the principle of acceleration, if the mortgagor fails to meet one installment payment, the entire balance is due immediately, giving the mortgagee the right to collect the full amount. A clause allowing acceleration must be exercised in good faith. In this case, Grasso refused to make four installment payments before Medina accelerated the debt. Waiting through four missed payments would probably indicate good faith on Medina's part.

6. No. A reverse mortgage is a type of loan that allows home owners over the age of sixty-two to convert some of the equity in their home into

cash. The LaFrenzes were fifty-eight years old.

7. Yes. A purchase money security interest is a security interest taken by a lender or a seller of an item to secure its price.

8. Yes. A secured party who has possession of the collateral must take reasonable care of the property. The debtor must reimburse the secured party for any money spent to take care of the property.

9. When a financing statement includes crops, the statement must also contain a description of the real estate involved. Silvia and Avitto neglected to include such a description in their agreement.

10. No. Collateral may be repossessed without going to court if it can be done without causing a disturbance. Otherwise, the creditor must use legal process.

Chapter 32
Legal Concepts

1.	F	6.	T	11.	T
2.	T	7.	T	12.	F
3.	F	8.	F	13.	F
4.	T	9.	T	14.	F
5.	F	10.	F	15.	T

Language of the Law

1.	k	6.	i
2.	c	7.	l
3.	h	8.	n
4.	b or i	9.	e
5.	a	10.	d

Applying the Law

1. Involuntary petitions cannot be filed against farmers, so they were rejected.

2. No. The automatic stay provision prohibits creditors from filing lawsuits against the debtor even if a suit is filed in a court other than the one handling the bankruptcy.

3. Yes. Any and all debts incurred in the administration of a bankruptcy proceeding are paid off before any other unsecured debts.

4. Yes. Exemptions can be doubled for married couples who file jointly.

5. No. Debtors cannot discharge any cash advances that total more than $1,000 if those advances were obtained within twenty days of the order for relief.

6. Bennet and Cooper should file under Chapter 11. Under Chapter 11, they can retain control of the business as debtors-in-possession while their debts are being reorganized. The cannot use Chapter 13 because it is open to individuals only. They cannot use Chapter 12 because it is open to family farmers only.

7. No. The primary committee set up to work with a debtor under Chapter 11 usually consists of the debtor's unsecured creditors. St. Clair is a secured creditor.

8. No. Chapter 12 is only available to family farmers. A family farmer is defined as one who receives more than one-half of his or her income from the farm. Bowers received only one-fourth of her income from the farm.

9. Chapter 13 is open to individual debtors only. Neither corporations nor partnerships can file under Chapter 13.

10. Only voluntary filings are permitted under Chapter 13.

Chapter 33
Legal Concepts

1.	F	6.	T	11.	F
2.	T	7.	T	12.	T
3.	F	8.	T	13.	F
4.	F	9.	F	14.	T
5.	F	10.	F	15.	F

Language of the Law

1. j
2. d
3. a
4. f
5. k
6. g
7. h
8. i
9. e
10. c

Applying the Law

1. Because he has broad powers to run the store, Clark is a general agent.
2. Since he can bid on only one tract of land, Anderson is a special agent.
3. McMahon is a proprietor. The plumber is an independent contractor.
4. Gallery can sue Thomson Bakery under the theory of vicarious liability.
5. A principal cannot get out of a contract by using the minority of an agent as a shield.
6. Greggs is a partially disclosed principal.
7. Selan is an undisclosed principal.
8. The duty to maintain a safe airline is a nondelegable duty.
9. A negligent hiring may have occurred.
10. Harrison ratified the contract made by Macy.

Chapter 34
Legal Concepts

1. T
2. T
3. T
4. F
5. T
6. F
7. T
8. F
9. T
10. T
11. F
12. T
13. T
14. F
15. F

Language of the Law

1. e
2. d
3. f
4. b
5. g
6. i
7. h
8. j
9. a
10. c

Applying the Law

1. Yes. Henry disobeyed Palla's instructions.
2. Allen violated his duty of loyalty to Kerry.

3. Razor can take all of the money in McClain's account.
4. Olley can refuse to honor the appointment because he hired Hurley for his expertise in figuring out taxes.
5. Yes. Knowledge gained by an agent is imputed to the principal.
6. Gunderson acted correctly because attending the World Series was not necessary for the carrying out of his duties.
7. United has the duty to reimburse Thomson.
8. Wilson does not have to inform anyone since the termination was by operation of law.
9. No. The principal's funds cannot be commingled with the agent's funds.
10. Yes. Pearsal was within his rights because Huxley disobeyed his instructions.

Chapter 35
Legal Concepts

1. T
2. F
3. F
4. T
5. T
6. F
7. T
8. T
9. F
10. T
11. F
12. T
13. F
14. T
15. F

Language of the Law

1. i
2. h
3. d
4. c
5. e
6. k
7. f
8. b
9. g
10. j

Applying the Law

1. Under employment-at-will, the employer had the right to discharge Garfield at any time for any reason with or without notice.
2. Samuels may enter the grievance procedure.
3. Yes. Morley may have a wrongful discharge lawsuit based on implied contract. (Also accept promissory

estoppel as the theory for the lawsuit.)

4. No. Only the president of the company could alter the disclaimer's provisions.

5. Under implied covenant Hubble could file a wrongful discharge lawsuit based on the inherent unfairness of the employer's action.

6. Hegel would not be qualified to receive benefits since she turned down the job at the Canton Clinic.

7. The need for women to model women's swimwear is a bona fide occupational qualification.

8. Yes. Saying a worker is "overqualified" is just another way of saying that she is "too old."

9. The Portland Area School Board is incorrect because under Title VII of the Civil Rights Act of 1964 as amended in 1991, all victims of discrimination can collect compensatory and punitive damages.

10. Yes. The ADA forbids discrimination on the basis of a disability if the disabled person can do the essential functions of the job with "reasonable accommodations."

Chapter 36
Legal Concepts

1. T	6. F	11. T
2. F	7. F	12. T
3. F	8. T	13. F
4. F	9. F	14. T
5. T	10. F	15. T

Language of the Law

1. f	6. c
2. l	7. a
3. m	8. d
4. j	9. h
5. g	10. b

Applying the Law

1. Yes. This activity violates the Wagner Act.

2. Yes. This activity also violates the Wagner Act.

3. No. The NLRB has no jurisdiction over religious schools.

4. Constructive discharge.

5. This activity violates the Wagner Act.

6. No. The Taft-Hartley Act allows employers to express their views of unions.

7. The Taft-Hartley Act forbids featherbedding, which requires an employer to hire or keep more employees than are needed.

8. No. Under the Landrum-Griffin Act all employees must be allowed to participate in the running of the union.

9. No. Employers can also file complaints with the NLRB.

10. According to federal law, workers in the public sectors cannot strike.

Chapter 37
Legal Concepts

1. F	6. F	11. T
2. T	7. T	12. F
3. T	8. F	13. F
4. T	9. T	14. F
5. F	10. F	15. F

Language of the Law

1. k	6. l
2. h	7. d
3. g	8. a
4. e	9. i
5. j	10. b

Applying the Law

1. Strong was wrong because his share of the profits was in the form of rental payments.

2. Partner's personal property cannot be at risk until all partnership assets have been exhausted.

3. No. Partnership agreements do not have to be in writing.
4. No. Partnership property cannot be used to satisfy personal debts of a partner.
5. No. A partner can assign his or her share of the profits without dissolving the partnership.
6. Yes. The decision to buy a computer is an ordinary business decision requiring a majority of the partners. Since the vote was split, Robinson had no power to buy the computer, and did not have the right to be reimbursed.
7. No. The admission of a new partner requires the unanimous consent of all of the partners.
8. No. Wong was incorrect. The partners have joint and several liability here.
9. No. When a partnership can be operated at a loss, a court decree is required for a dissolution.
10. Schaps knew that he was dealing with a limited partnership and that Fletcher was a limited partner.

Chapter 38
Legal Concepts

1. F	6. F	11. F
2. T	7. T	12. F
3. T	8. F	13. F
4. T	9. F	14. T
5. F	10. T	15. T

Language of the Law

1. b	6. k
2. n	7. h
3. c	8. f
4. d	9. a
5. l	10. g

Applying the Law

1. Dynasoar will have to obtain a certificate of authority.
2. Granger is correct in stating that the filing of an operating agreement is desirable, but it is not required by law in most states.

3. Promoters are personally liable for contracts they negotiate for a yet-to-be-born corporation.
4. McKinley, Hinders, and Manning can use the doctrine of de facto corporation. De facto corporation exists if a valid incorporation statute is in effect in the state, if the parties have made a good faith attempt to incorporate, and have exercised corporate power.
5. The creditor used the doctrine of piercing the corporate veil.
6. The doctrine that will protect him is corporation by estoppel.
7. Virginia has no personal jurisdiction over the corporation.
8. No. A corporation pays dividends when the corporation elects to make such a distribution.
9. Marple owned cumulative preferred stock. Taft owned noncumulative preferred stock.
10. Amendment 14 to the U.S. Constitution allowed the corporation to sue the state, because the state had deprived the corporation of its property without due process.

Chapter 39
Legal Concepts

1. F	6. F	11. T
2. T	7. F	12. F
3. F	8. T	13. T
4. F	9. T	14. T
5. F	10. F	15. T

Language of the Law

1. g	6. b
2. k	7. c
3. o	8. l
4. e	9. d
5. j	10. m

Applying the Law

1. No. Directors are not entitled to notice of regularly scheduled board meetings.
2. The business judgment rule would protect Brickley. The rule says that the decisions of corporate managers will stand as long as the decisions are legal, made in good faith and with due care, and are in the best interests of the corporation.
3. The fairness rule will be used to judge Chicote's conduct because he personally profited from the decision.
4. The fairness rule will be used to judge Dunkin's conduct because he personally profited from the decision.
5. The fairness rule will be used to judge Finnegan's conduct because he personally profited from the decision.
6. Harding would support the theory of corporate democracy because he wants to see an increase in the shareholders' input into corporate decisions.
7. No. To be valid a voting trust must be in writing and must be filed with the corporation.
8. Pollard's shareholder proposal is too long. The maximum length is 500 words. Also, the proposal was not submitted 120 days before the next shareholders' meeting.
9. No. The exhaustion of internal remedies requirement applies to derivative suits. This is a direct suit.
10. Higgins would have the right to purchase 200 shares. This would mean that he would own a total of 400 shares and that his proportion of the ownership would have remained constant.

Chapter 40
Legal Concepts

1.	F	6.	T	11.	T
2.	F	7.	T	12.	T
3.	T	8.	T	13.	F
4.	F	9.	F	14.	F
5.	F	10.	T	15.	T

Language of the Law

1.	o	6.	l
2.	h	7.	b
3.	f	8.	i
4.	j	9.	a
5.	n	10.	k

Applying the Law

1. No. A security is a money investment which expects a return solely because of another person's efforts. Roth's investors do nothing but contribute money here. They then receive a return on that investment.
2. Holley lost the suit because information in proxy solicitations must be displayed prominently.
3. No. An agreement to divide territories is a violation of antitrust law even if it helps the parties compete against other parties outside the agreement.
4. Varnes has correctly objected to this arrangement because it is a tying agreement.
5. No. An asset acquisition does not require the approval of the shareholders of the corporation that is buying the assets.
6. Schuler could engage in a stock acquisition (aka a takeover bid).
7. The board of directors could search for a white knight to outbid Schuler.
8. Saunders was unsuccessful because the debts of the corporation do not pass to the party purchasing the assets of that corporation.
9. No. Violations of the Environmental Protection Act extend to accidental pollution.
10. The state could initiate a *quo warranto* action.

Chapter 41
Legal Concepts

1.	F	6.	F
2.	T	7.	F
3.	F	8.	T
4.	T	9.	T
5.	F	10.	F

Language of the Law

1. c	6. e
2. g	7. i
3. n	8. a
4. k	9. j
5. b	10. f

Applying the Law

1. The state cannot prevent someone from practicing accounting as a profession. The state can only prevent individuals without the proper education and experience from calling themselves CPA's and PA's.
2. Ackerman has issued a qualified opinion.
3. Baird has issued an adverse opinion.
4. Gibson is liable to McCoy because McCoy is an actually named third party.
5. Jameson is incorrect because his actions are fraudulent. An accountant who prepares a fraudulent financial statement is liable to anyone who can be reasonably foreseen as relying on that statement.
6. Podman is correct because Jefferson ignored her work and used his own calculations.
7. Renkar violated the duty of loyalty.
8. Attorneys are not held liable to third parties because the attorney's responsibility is tied closely with the interests of the client.
9. The consent form will not protect DeLong or the hospital because Passarelli was deliberately misled as to its nature.
10. Yes. Expert testimony is not needed when the action under consideration is within the common knowledge of all people.

Chapter 42
Legal Concepts

1. F	6. T	11. F
2. F	7. F	12. F
3. F	8. F	13. T
4. T	9. F	14. F
5. F	10. T	15. F

Language of the Law

1. b	6. e
2. j	7. n
3. h	8. k
4. m	9. p
5. f	10. a

Applying the Law

1. No claim can be made that "Taxes 'R Fun" is a trade secret since it has been placed on the open market.
2. The refusal was reversed because a device can be patented if the computer program is just a part of the overall process.
3. The patent was refused because it is simply a mathematical formula.
4. No. Hilliard is incorrect. Both the E-Sign Act and the Uniform Electronic Transactions Act give electronic contracts the same force as written contracts produced on paper documents.
5. No. Cybertrespass is the use of a computer as an instrumentality to commit any crime that is already part of the state's conventional criminal code.
6. No. Jason is incorrect. Cyberterrorism involves operating a computer to disrupt or destroy one or more crucial elements of the national electronic infrastructure. This would include a city-wide water system. Also, physical harm would not be needed.
7. No. Carol is incorrect. Cybervandalism does not require that the perpetrator gain from the interference with a computer system.
8. Amy is correct and Nick is wrong. The EU and the USA approach privacy and computers in two very different ways. The EU assumes that privacy violations will occur and provides a way to deal with them, while the USA tries to prevent privacy violations.
9. Vernon is correct. The Anticybersquatting Consumer Protection Act was designed to target the type of scheme that Sam has planned here.

10. Ben's plan will not work because the Economic Espionage Act does not provide for any civil lawsuits.

Chapter 43
Legal Concepts

1. F	6. F	11. T
2. T	7. T	12. F
3. F	8. F	13. F
4. F	9. F	14. F
5. F	10. F	15. T

Language of the Law

1. i	6. f
2. e	7. c
3. h	8. d
4. k	9. j
5. a	10. b

Applying the Law

1. No. Under the rules of the ICJ, any member nation can file a case with the ICJ asking for an advisory opinion.
2. No. A nation is not bound by a United Nations Convention until it is officially adopted by that nation's government.
3. Pierre is incorrect. The Directive on the Protection of Consumers in Respect of Distance Contracts (ECD) will protect Jean-Luc. He will be able to cancel the transaction within seven business days.
4. No. The court will hold that the increased cost and the difficulty of performance did not constitute impracticality. The court would probably also say that when a company like Transglobal enters a contract that is related to the international situation, it is wise for that company to be aware of the international conditions in all areas of the globe that may affect the contract.
5. The war may be described as failing categories 1, 2, 5, and 6: (1) The war may not have been prompted by a just cause because neither the Iraqi weapons of mass destruction nor the advanced Iraqi nuclear program was found to be in existence as believed by the American administration;

(2) whether the right intention was used to wage the war is unclear again because neither the Iraqi weapons of mass destruction nor the Iraqi nuclear program was ever uncovered; (5) proportionality may have been violated because the intended results, the removal of the weapons and the destruction of the nuclear program, were not proportionate to results, that is, the deaths of thousands of Iraqi citizens, the deaths or wounding of thousands of coalition soldiers, the destruction of the infrastructure of the entire country, and the bloody civil conflict that followed the invasion, especially since neither the weapons nor the nuclear program actually existed; finally, (6) the war may not have been a last resort, since several nations were willing to continue the inspection process, which might very well have revealed the truth of the matter, that is, that no weapons of mass destruction actually existed and that no nuclear program was in operation, thus saving thousands of lives and preserving the infrastructure of the country. The war passed criteria 3 and 4: (3) the war was instituted by a competent authority because it was instigated by the commander-in-chief of the US military with a vote of approval from the American Congress; and (4) there was a probability of success, due to American military superiority.
6. Yes. As a citizen of the EU, Maria has a legal cause of action against Chardin under the EU Data Protection Directive.
7. Friedrich is correct. Three EU member nations, the United Kingdom, Denmark, and Sweden have not adopted the euro.
8. No. Only sovereign nations have legal standing to bring a case to the ICJ.
9. The United States is correct. The interpretation of treaties is under the jurisdiction of the ICJ.
10. Yes. The ICJ does have the power to issue advisory opinions.